2023 DIARY

PERSONAL INFORMATION

NAME

ADDRESS

E-MAIL

TEL

MOBILE

2023 YEAR PLANNER

	MON	TUE	WED	THUR	FRI	SAT	SUN	MON	TUE	WED	THUR	FRI	SAT	SUN	MON	TUE	WED	THUR	FRI	SAT	SUN
JAN							01	02	03	04	05	06	07	08	09	10	11	12	13	14	15
	WK 52							WK 1							WK 2						
FEB			01	02	03	04	05	06	07	08	09	10	11	12	13	14	15	16	17	18	19
	WK 5							WK 6							WK 7						
MAR			01	02	03	04	05	06	07	08	09	10	11	12	13	14	15	16	17	18	19
	WK 9							WK 10							WK 11						
APR						01	02	03	04	05	06	07	08	09	10	11	12	13	14	15	16
	WK 13							WK 14							WK 15						
MAY	01	02	03	04	05	06	07	08	09	10	11	12	13	14	15	16	17	18	19	20	21
	WK 18							WK 19							WK 20						
JUN				01	02	03	04	05	06	07	08	09	10	11	12	13	14	15	16	17	18
	WK 22							WK 23							WK 24						
JUL						01	02	03	04	05	06	07	08	09	10	11	12	13	14	15	16
	WK 26							WK 27							WK 28						
AUG		01	02	03	04	05	06	07	08	09	10	11	12	13	14	15	16	17	18	19	20
	WK 31							WK 32							WK 33						
SEP					01	02	03	04	05	06	07	08	09	10	11	12	13	14	15	16	17
	WK 35							WK 36							WK 37						
OCT							01	02	03	04	05	06	07	08	09	10	11	12	13	14	15
	WK 39							WK 40							WK 41						
NOV			01	02	03	04	05	06	07	08	09	10	11	12	13	14	15	16	17	18	19
	WK 44							WK 45							WK 46						
DEC					01	02	03	04	05	06	07	08	09	10	11	12	13	14	15	16	17
	WK 48							WK 49							WK 50						

MON	TUE	WED	THUR	FRI	SAT	SUN	MON	TUE	WED	THUR	FRI	SAT	SUN	MON	TUE	WED	THUR	FRI	SAT	SUN	
16	17	18	19	20	21	22	23	24	25	26	27	28	29	30	31						JAN
WK 3							WK 4							WK 5							
20	21	22	23	24	25	26	27	28													FEB
WK 8							WK 9														
20	21	22	23	24	25	26	27	28	29	30	31										MAR
WK 12							WK 13														
17	18	19	20	21	22	23	24	25	26	27	28	29	30								APR
WK 16							WK 17														
22	23	24	25	26	27	28	29	30	31												MAY
WK 21							WK 22														
19	20	21	22	23	24	25	26	27	28	29	30										JUN
WK 25							WK 26														
17	18	19	20	21	22	23	24	25	26	27	28	29	30	31							JUL
WK 29							WK 30							WK 31							
21	22	23	24	25	26	27	28	29	30	31											AUG
WK 34							WK 35														
18	19	20	21	22	23	24	25	26	27	28	29	30									SEP
WK 38							WK 39														
16	17	18	19	20	21	22	23	24	25	26	27	28	29	30	31						OCT
WK 42							WK 43							WK 44							
20	21	22	23	24	25	26	27	28	29	30											NOV
WK 47							WK 48														
18	19	20	21	22	23	24	25	26	27	28	29	30	31								DEC
WK 51							WK 52														

2023 NOTABLE DATES

JANUARY	01	SUN	NEW YEAR'S DAY
	02	MON	NEW YEAR'S DAY [OBSERVED]
	03	TUE	2ND JANUARY [SUBSTITUTE DAY] (SCOTLAND); DAY AFTER NEW YEAR'S DAY (NZ)
	06	FRI	EPIPHANY
	15	SUN	MAKAR SANKRANTI
	16	MON	MARTIN LUTHER KING JR. DAY (USA)
	22	SUN	CHINESE NEW YEAR (YEAR OF THE RABBIT)
	25	WED	BURNS NIGHT (SCOTLAND)
	26	THUR	AUSTRALIA DAY (AUS); VASANT PANCHAMI
FEBRUARY	06	MON	TU B'SHEVAT (ARBOR DAY); WAITANGI DAY (NZ)
	14	TUE	VALENTINE'S DAY
	18	SAT	MAHA SHIVARATRI; ISRA AND MI'RAJ
	20	MON	PRESIDENTS' DAY (USA)
	21	TUE	SHROVE TUESDAY
	22	WED	ASH WEDNESDAY
MARCH	01	WED	ST DAVID'S DAY (WALES)
	07	TUE	PURIM
	08	WED	HOLI
	17	FRI	ST PATRICK'S DAY (N. IRELAND & ROI)
	19	SUN	MOTHER'S DAY
	20	MON	VERNAL EQUINOX
	22	WED	RAMADAN STARTS
	26	SUN	BRITISH SUMMER TIME BEGINS
	30	THUR	RAMA NAVAMI
APRIL	02	SUN	PALM SUNDAY
	06	THUR	MAUNDY THURSDAY; FIRST DAY OF PASSOVER
	07	FRI	GOOD FRIDAY
	08	SAT	HOLY SATURDAY
	09	SUN	EASTER SUNDAY
	10	MON	EASTER MONDAY (UK, ROI, CAN, AUS, NZ)
	13	THUR	LAST DAY OF PASSOVER
	18	TUE	YOM HASHOAH; LAYLATUL QADR (NIGHT OF POWER)
	22	SAT	EID AL-FITR
	23	SUN	ST GEORGE'S DAY; SHAKESPEARE DAY
	25	TUES	ANZAC DAY (AUS, NZ)
	26	WED	YOM HAATZMAUT
MAY	01	MON	MAY BANK HOLIDAY (UK & ROI)
	09	TUE	LAG B'OMER
	18	THUR	ASCENSION DAY
	22	MON	VICTORIA DAY (CAN)
	26	FRI	SHAVUOT
	28	SUN	PENTECOST
	29	MON	SPRING BANK HOLIDAY (UK); WHIT MONDAY; MEMORIAL DAY (USA)
JUNE	04	SUN	TRINITY SUNDAY
	05	MON	JUNE BANK HOLIDAY (ROI); QUEEN'S BIRTHDAY (NZ)
	08	THUR	CORPUS CHRISTI
	10	SAT	QUEEN'S OFFICIAL BIRTHDAY (UK)
	18	SUN	FATHER'S DAY
	21	WED	SUMMER SOLSTICE
	22	THUR	WINDRUSH DAY
	24	SAT	ARMED FORCES DAY (UK)
	29	THUR	EID UL-ADHA

2023 NOTABLE DATES

JULY	01	SAT	CANADA DAY (CAN)
	04	TUE	INDEPENDENCE DAY (USA)
	12	WED	BATTLE OF THE BOYNE (N. IRELAND)
	19	WED	MUHARRAM/ISLAMIC NEW YEAR
	27	THUR	TISHA B'AV
	28	FRI	ASHURA

AUGUST	07	MON	SUMMER BANK HOLIDAY (SCOTLAND & ROI)
	15	TUE	ASSUMPTION OF MARY
	28	MON	SUMMER BANK HOLIDAY (UK EXCEPT SCOTLAND)
	30	WED	RAKSHA BANDHAN

SEPTEMBER	04	MON	LABOR DAY (USA, CAN)
	06	WED	JANMASHTAMI
	16	SAT	ROSH HASHANA
	19	TUE	GANESH CHATURTHI
	23	SAT	AUTUMN EQUINOX
	25	MON	YOM KIPPUR
	27	WED	MILAD UN NABI (MAWLID)/THE PROPHET'S BIRTHDAY
	30	SAT	FIRST DAY OF SUKKOT

OCTOBER	04	WED	FEAST OF ST FRANCIS OF ASSISI
	06	FRI	HOSHANA RABBAH
	07	SAT	SHEMINI ATZERET
	08	SUN	SIMCHAT TORAH
	09	MON	THANKSGIVING DAY (CAN); COLUMBUS DAY (USA)
	15	SUN	NAVRATRI
	23	MON	DUSSEHRA; LABOUR DAY (NZ)
	29	SUN	BRITISH SUMMER TIME ENDS
	30	MON	OCTOBER BANK HOLIDAY (ROI)
	31	TUE	HALLOWEEN

NOVEMBER	01	WED	ALL SAINTS' DAY
	02	THUR	ALL SOULS' DAY
	05	SUN	GUY FAWKES NIGHT
	10	FRI	VETERANS DAY [OBSERVED](USA)
	11	SAT	REMEMBRANCE DAY (CAN, AUS); VETERANS DAY (USA)
	12	SUN	REMEMBRANCE SUNDAY; DIWALI/DEEPAVALI
	23	THUR	THANKSGIVING DAY (USA)
	30	THUR	ST ANDREW'S DAY (SCOTLAND)

DECEMBER	03	SUN	FIRST SUNDAY OF ADVENT
	08	FRI	FEAST OF THE IMMACULATE CONCEPTION; FIRST DAY OF HANUKKAH
	15	FRI	LAST DAY OF HANUKKAH
	22	FRI	WINTER SOLSTICE
	24	SUN	CHRISTMAS EVE
	25	MON	CHRISTMAS DAY
	26	TUES	BOXING DAY; ST. STEPHEN'S DAY (ROI)
	31	SUN	NEW YEAR'S EVE

2023

JANUARY

M	T	W	T	F	S	S
						01
02	03	04	05	06	07	08
09	10	11	12	13	14	15
16	17	18	19	20	21	22
23	24	25	26	27	28	29
30	31					

FEBRUARY

M	T	W	T	F	S	S
		01	02	03	04	05
06	07	08	09	10	11	12
13	14	15	16	17	18	19
20	21	22	23	24	25	26
27	28					

MARCH

M	T	W	T	F	S	S
		01	02	03	04	05
06	07	08	09	10	11	12
13	14	15	16	17	18	19
20	21	22	23	24	25	26
27	28	29	30	31		

APRIL

M	T	W	T	F	S	S
					01	02
03	04	05	06	07	08	09
10	11	12	13	14	15	16
17	18	19	20	21	22	23
24	25	26	27	28	29	30

MAY

M	T	W	T	F	S	S
01	02	03	04	05	06	07
08	09	10	11	12	13	14
15	16	17	18	19	20	21
22	23	24	25	26	27	28
29	30	31				

JUNE

M	T	W	T	F	S	S
			01	02	03	04
05	06	07	08	09	10	11
12	13	14	15	16	17	18
19	20	21	22	23	24	25
26	27	28	29	30		

JULY

M	T	W	T	F	S	S
					01	02
03	04	05	06	07	08	09
10	11	12	13	14	15	16
17	18	19	20	21	22	23
24	25	26	27	28	29	30
31						

AUGUST

M	T	W	T	F	S	S
	01	02	03	04	05	06
07	08	09	10	11	12	13
14	15	16	17	18	19	20
21	22	23	24	25	26	27
28	29	30	31			

SEPTEMBER

M	T	W	T	F	S	S
				01	02	03
04	05	06	07	08	09	10
11	12	13	14	15	16	17
18	19	20	21	22	23	24
25	26	27	28	29	30	

OCTOBER

M	T	W	T	F	S	S
						01
02	03	04	05	06	07	08
09	10	11	12	13	14	15
16	17	18	19	20	21	22
23	24	25	26	27	28	29
30	31					

NOVEMBER

M	T	W	T	F	S	S
		01	02	03	04	05
06	07	08	09	10	11	12
13	14	15	16	17	18	19
20	21	22	23	24	25	26
27	28	29	30			

DECEMBER

M	T	W	T	F	S	S
				01	02	03
04	05	06	07	08	09	10
11	12	13	14	15	16	17
18	19	20	21	22	23	24
25	26	27	28	29	30	31

THURSDAY 29

THINGS TO DO/NOTES

FRIDAY 30

THINGS TO DO/NOTES

NEW YEAR'S EVE

SATURDAY 31

THINGS TO DO/NOTES

NEW YEAR'S DAY

SUNDAY 01

THINGS TO DO/NOTES

JULY								AUGUST								SEPTEMBER								OCTOBER								NOVEMBER								DECEMBER						
M	T	W	T	F	S	S		M	T	W	T	F	S	S		M	T	W	T	F	S	S		M	T	W	T	F	S	S		M	T	W	T	F	S	S		M	T	W	T	F	S	S
					01	02			01	02	03	04	05	06						01	02	03							01			01	02	03	04	05						01	02	03
03	04	05	06	07	08	09		07	08	09	10	11	12	13		04	05	06	07	08	09	10		02	03	04	05	06	07	08		06	07	08	09	10	11	12		04	05	06	07	08	09	10
10	11	12	13	14	15	16		14	15	16	17	18	19	20		11	12	13	14	15	16	17		09	10	11	12	13	14	15		13	14	15	16	17	18	19		11	12	13	14	15	16	17
17	18	19	20	21	22	23		21	22	23	24	25	26	27		18	19	20	21	22	23	24		16	17	18	19	20	21	22		20	21	22	23	24	25	26		18	19	20	21	22	23	24
24	25	26	27	28	29	30		28	29	30	31					25	26	27	28	29	30			23	24	25	26	27	28	29		27	28	29	30					25	26	27	28	29	30	31
31																							30	31																				

JANUARY
WEEK 01

02 MONDAY
THINGS TO DO/NOTES

NEW YEAR'S DAY [OBSERVED]

03 TUESDAY
THINGS TO DO/NOTES

2ND JANUARY [SUBSTITUTE DAY] (SCOTLAND); DAY AFTER NEW YEAR'S DAY (NZ)

04 WEDNESDAY
THINGS TO DO/NOTES

JANUARY						
M	T	W	T	F	S	S
						01
02	03	04	05	06	07	08
09	10	11	12	13	14	15
16	17	18	19	20	21	22
23	24	25	26	27	28	29
30	31					

FEBRUARY						
M	T	W	T	F	S	S
		01	02	03	04	05
06	07	08	09	10	11	12
13	14	15	16	17	18	19
20	21	22	23	24	25	26
27	28					

MARCH						
M	T	W	T	F	S	S
		01	02	03	04	05
06	07	08	09	10	11	12
13	14	15	16	17	18	19
20	21	22	23	24	25	26
27	28	29	30	31		

APRIL						
M	T	W	T	F	S	S
					01	02
03	04	05	06	07	08	09
10	11	12	13	14	15	16
17	18	19	20	21	22	23
24	25	26	27	28	29	30

MAY						
M	T	W	T	F	S	S
01	02	03	04	05	06	07
08	09	10	11	12	13	14
15	16	17	18	19	20	21
22	23	24	25	26	27	28
29	30	31				

JUNE						
M	T	W	T	F	S	S
			01	02	03	04
05	06	07	08	09	10	11
12	13	14	15	16	17	18
19	20	21	22	23	24	25
26	27	28	29	30		

THURSDAY 05

THINGS TO DO/NOTES

EPIPHANY

FRIDAY 06

THINGS TO DO/NOTES

SATURDAY 07

THINGS TO DO/NOTES

SUNDAY 08

THINGS TO DO/NOTES

JULY								AUGUST								SEPTEMBER								OCTOBER								NOVEMBER								DECEMBER						
M	T	W	T	F	S	S		M	T	W	T	F	S	S		M	T	W	T	F	S	S		M	T	W	T	F	S	S		M	T	W	T	F	S	S		M	T	W	T	F	S	S
					01	02			01	02	03	04	05	06						01	02	03							01				01	02	03	04	05						01	02	03
03	04	05	06	07	08	09		07	08	09	10	11	12	13		04	05	06	07	08	09	10		02	03	04	05	06	07	08		06	07	08	09	10	11	12		04	05	06	07	08	09	10
10	11	12	13	14	15	16		14	15	16	17	18	19	20		11	12	13	14	15	16	17		09	10	11	12	13	14	15		13	14	15	16	17	18	19		11	12	13	14	15	16	17
17	18	19	20	21	22	23		21	22	23	24	25	26	27		18	19	20	21	22	23	24		16	17	18	19	20	21	22		20	21	22	23	24	25	26		18	19	20	21	22	23	24
24	25	26	27	28	29	30		28	29	30	31					25	26	27	28	29	30			23	24	25	26	27	28	29		27	28	29	30					25	26	27	28	29	30	31
31																							30	31																				

JANUARY
WEEK 02

09 MONDAY
THINGS TO DO/NOTES

10 TUESDAY
THINGS TO DO/NOTES

11 WEDNESDAY
THINGS TO DO/NOTES

JANUARY								FEBRUARY								MARCH								APRIL								MAY								JUNE						
M	T	W	T	F	S	S		M	T	W	T	F	S	S		M	T	W	T	F	S	S		M	T	W	T	F	S	S		M	T	W	T	F	S	S		M	T	W	T	F	S	S
						01				01	02	03	04	05				01	02	03	04	05						01	02		01	02	03	04	05	06	07						01	02	03	04
02	03	04	05	06	07	08		06	07	08	09	10	11	12		06	07	08	09	10	11	12		03	04	05	06	07	08	09		08	09	10	11	12	13	14		05	06	07	08	09	10	11
09	10	11	12	13	14	15		13	14	15	16	17	18	19		13	14	15	16	17	18	19		10	11	12	13	14	15	16		15	16	17	18	19	20	21		12	13	14	15	16	17	18
16	17	18	19	20	21	22		20	21	22	23	24	25	26		20	21	22	23	24	25	26		17	18	19	20	21	22	23		22	23	24	25	26	27	28		19	20	21	22	23	24	25
23	24	25	26	27	28	29		27	28							27	28	29	30	31				24	25	26	27	28	29	30		29	30	31						26	27	28	29	30		
30	31																																											

THURSDAY 12
THINGS TO DO/NOTES

FRIDAY 13
THINGS TO DO/NOTES

SATURDAY 14
THINGS TO DO/NOTES

MAKAR SANKRANTI

SUNDAY 15
THINGS TO DO/NOTES

JULY						
M	T	W	T	F	S	S
				01	02	
03	04	05	06	07	08	09
10	11	12	13	14	15	16
17	18	19	20	21	22	23
24	25	26	27	28	29	30
31						

AUGUST						
M	T	W	T	F	S	S
01	02	03	04	05	06	
07	08	09	10	11	12	13
14	15	16	17	18	19	20
21	22	23	24	25	26	27
28	29	30	31			

SEPTEMBER						
M	T	W	T	F	S	S
			01	02	03	
04	05	06	07	08	09	10
11	12	13	14	15	16	17
18	19	20	21	22	23	24
25	26	27	28	29	30	

OCTOBER						
M	T	W	T	F	S	S
					01	
02	03	04	05	06	07	08
09	10	11	12	13	14	15
16	17	18	19	20	21	22
23	24	25	26	27	28	29
30	31					

NOVEMBER						
M	T	W	T	F	S	S
	01	02	03	04	05	
06	07	08	09	10	11	12
13	14	15	16	17	18	19
20	21	22	23	24	25	26
27	28	29	30			

DECEMBER						
M	T	W	T	F	S	S
			01	02	03	
04	05	06	07	08	09	10
11	12	13	14	15	16	17
18	19	20	21	22	23	24
25	26	27	28	29	30	31

JANUARY
WEEK 03

16 MONDAY
THINGS TO DO/NOTES

MARTIN LUTHER KING JR. DAY (USA)

17 TUESDAY
THINGS TO DO/NOTES

18 WEDNESDAY
THINGS TO DO/NOTES

JANUARY	FEBRUARY	MARCH	APRIL	MAY	JUNE
M T W T F S S	M T W T F S S	M T W T F S S	M T W T F S S	M T W T F S S	M T W T F S S
01	01 02 03 04 05	01 02 03 04 05	01 02	01 02 03 04 05 06 07	01 02 03 04
02 03 04 05 06 07 08	06 07 08 09 10 11 12	06 07 08 09 10 11 12	03 04 05 06 07 08 09	08 09 10 11 12 13 14	05 06 07 08 09 10 11
09 10 11 12 13 14 15	13 14 15 16 17 18 19	13 14 15 16 17 18 19	10 11 12 13 14 15 16	15 16 17 18 19 20 21	12 13 14 15 16 17 18
16 17 18 19 20 21 22	20 21 22 23 24 25 26	20 21 22 23 24 25 26	17 18 19 20 21 22 23	22 23 24 25 26 27 28	19 20 21 22 23 24 25
23 24 25 26 27 28 29	27 28	27 28 29 30 31	24 25 26 27 28 29 30	29 30 31	26 27 28 29 30
30 31					

JANUARY

THURSDAY 19
THINGS TO DO/NOTES

FRIDAY 20
THINGS TO DO/NOTES

SATURDAY 21
THINGS TO DO/NOTES

CHINESE NEW YEAR (YEAR OF THE RABBIT)

SUNDAY 22
THINGS TO DO/NOTES

JULY	AUGUST	SEPTEMBER	OCTOBER	NOVEMBER	DECEMBER
M T W T F S S	M T W T F S S	M T W T F S S	M T W T F S S	M T W T F S S	M T W T F S S
01 02	01 02 03 04 05 06	01 02 03	01	01 02 03 04 05	01 02 03
03 04 05 06 07 08 09	07 08 09 10 11 12 13	04 05 06 07 08 09 10	02 03 04 05 06 07 08	06 07 08 09 10 11 12	04 05 06 07 08 09 10
10 11 12 13 14 15 16	14 15 16 17 18 19 20	11 12 13 14 15 16 17	09 10 11 12 13 14 15	13 14 15 16 17 18 19	11 12 13 14 15 16 17
17 18 19 20 21 22 23	21 22 23 24 25 26 27	18 19 20 21 22 23 24	16 17 18 19 20 21 22	20 21 22 23 24 25 26	18 19 20 21 22 23 24
24 25 26 27 28 29 30	28 29 30 31	25 26 27 28 29 30	23 24 25 26 27 28 29	27 28 29 30	25 26 27 28 29 30 31
31			30 31		

JANUARY

23 MONDAY
THINGS TO DO/NOTES

24 TUESDAY
THINGS TO DO/NOTES

25 WEDNESDAY
THINGS TO DO/NOTES

BURNS NIGHT (SCOTLAND)

JANUARY								FEBRUARY								MARCH								APRIL								MAY								JUNE						
M	T	W	T	F	S	S		M	T	W	T	F	S	S		M	T	W	T	F	S	S		M	T	W	T	F	S	S		M	T	W	T	F	S	S		M	T	W	T	F	S	S
						01				01	02	03	04	05				01	02	03	04	05							01	02		01	02	03	04	05	06	07						01	02	03	04
02	03	04	05	06	07	08		06	07	08	09	10	11	12		06	07	08	09	10	11	12		03	04	05	06	07	08	09		08	09	10	11	12	13	14		05	06	07	08	09	10	11
09	10	11	12	13	14	15		13	14	15	16	17	18	19		13	14	15	16	17	18	19		10	11	12	13	14	15	16		15	16	17	18	19	20	21		12	13	14	15	16	17	18
16	17	18	19	20	21	22		20	21	22	23	24	25	26		20	21	22	23	24	25	26		17	18	19	20	21	22	23		22	23	24	25	26	27	28		19	20	21	22	23	24	25
23	24	25	26	27	28	29		27	28							27	28	29	30	31				24	25	26	27	28	29	30		29	30	31						26	27	28	29	30		
30	31																																											

AUSTRALIA DAY (AUS); VASANT PANCHAMI

THURSDAY 26
THINGS TO DO/NOTES

FRIDAY 27
THINGS TO DO/NOTES

SATURDAY 28
THINGS TO DO/NOTES

SUNDAY 29
THINGS TO DO/NOTES

JANUARY
WEEK 05

FEBRUARY

30 MONDAY
THINGS TO DO/NOTES

31 TUESDAY
THINGS TO DO/NOTES

01 WEDNESDAY
THINGS TO DO/NOTES

JANUARY							FEBRUARY							MARCH							APRIL							MAY							JUNE						
M	T	W	T	F	S	S	M	T	W	T	F	S	S	M	T	W	T	F	S	S	M	T	W	T	F	S	S	M	T	W	T	F	S	S	M	T	W	T	F	S	S
						01			01	02	03	04	05			01	02	03	04	05						01	02	01	02	03	04	05	06	07					01	02	03	04
02	03	04	05	06	07	08	06	07	08	09	10	11	12	06	07	08	09	10	11	12	03	04	05	06	07	08	09	08	09	10	11	12	13	14	05	06	07	08	09	10	11
09	10	11	12	13	14	15	13	14	15	16	17	18	19	13	14	15	16	17	18	19	10	11	12	13	14	15	16	15	16	17	18	19	20	21	12	13	14	15	16	17	18
16	17	18	19	20	21	22	20	21	22	23	24	25	26	20	21	22	23	24	25	26	17	18	19	20	21	22	23	22	23	24	25	26	27	28	19	20	21	22	23	24	25
23	24	25	26	27	28	29	27	28						27	28	29	30	31			24	25	26	27	28	29	30	29	30	31					26	27	28	29	30		
30	31																																								

THURSDAY 02
THINGS TO DO/NOTES

FRIDAY 03
THINGS TO DO/NOTES

SATURDAY 04
THINGS TO DO/NOTES

SUNDAY 05
THINGS TO DO/NOTES

JULY						
M	T	W	T	F	S	S
				01	02	
03	04	05	06	07	08	09
10	11	12	13	14	15	16
17	18	19	20	21	22	23
24	25	26	27	28	29	30
31						

AUGUST						
M	T	W	T	F	S	S
01	02	03	04	05	06	
07	08	09	10	11	12	13
14	15	16	17	18	19	20
21	22	23	24	25	26	27
28	29	30	31			

SEPTEMBER						
M	T	W	T	F	S	S
				01	02	03
04	05	06	07	08	09	10
11	12	13	14	15	16	17
18	19	20	21	22	23	24
25	26	27	28	29	30	

OCTOBER						
M	T	W	T	F	S	S
						01
02	03	04	05	06	07	08
09	10	11	12	13	14	15
16	17	18	19	20	21	22
23	24	25	26	27	28	29
30	31					

NOVEMBER						
M	T	W	T	F	S	S
	01	02	03	04	05	
06	07	08	09	10	11	12
13	14	15	16	17	18	19
20	21	22	23	24	25	26
27	28	29	30			

DECEMBER						
M	T	W	T	F	S	S
				01	02	03
04	05	06	07	08	09	10
11	12	13	14	15	16	17
18	19	20	21	22	23	24
25	26	27	28	29	30	31

06 MONDAY

THINGS TO DO/NOTES

TU B'SHEVAT (ARBOR DAY); WAITANGI DAY (NZ)

07 TUESDAY

THINGS TO DO/NOTES

08 WEDNESDAY

THINGS TO DO/NOTES

JANUARY	FEBRUARY	MARCH	APRIL	MAY	JUNE
M T W T F S S	M T W T F S S	M T W T F S S	M T W T F S S	M T W T F S S	M T W T F S S
01	01 02 03 04 05	01 02 03 04 05	01 02	01 02 03 04 05 06 07	01 02 03 04
02 03 04 05 06 07 08	06 07 08 09 10 11 12	06 07 08 09 10 11 12	03 04 05 06 07 08 09	08 09 10 11 12 13 14	05 06 07 08 09 10 11
09 10 11 12 13 14 15	13 14 15 16 17 18 19	13 14 15 16 17 18 19	10 11 12 13 14 15 16	15 16 17 18 19 20 21	12 13 14 15 16 17 18
16 17 18 19 20 21 22	20 21 22 23 24 25 26	20 21 22 23 24 25 26	17 18 19 20 21 22 23	22 23 24 25 26 27 28	19 20 21 22 23 24 25
23 24 25 26 27 28 29	27 28	27 28 29 30 31	24 25 26 27 28 29 30	29 30 31	26 27 28 29 30
30 31					

THURSDAY 09
THINGS TO DO/NOTES

FRIDAY 10
THINGS TO DO/NOTES

SATURDAY 11
THINGS TO DO/NOTES

SUNDAY 12
THINGS TO DO/NOTES

JULY								AUGUST								SEPTEMBER								OCTOBER								NOVEMBER								DECEMBER						
M	T	W	T	F	S	S		M	T	W	T	F	S	S		M	T	W	T	F	S	S		M	T	W	T	F	S	S		M	T	W	T	F	S	S		M	T	W	T	F	S	S	
					01	02			01	02	03	04	05	06						01	02	03							01			01	02	03	04	05						01	02	03	
03	04	05	06	07	08	09		07	08	09	10	11	12	13		04	05	06	07	08	09	10		02	03	04	05	06	07	08		06	07	08	09	10	11	12		04	05	06	07	08	09	10	
10	11	12	13	14	15	16		14	15	16	17	18	19	20		11	12	13	14	15	16	17		09	10	11	12	13	14	15		13	14	15	16	17	18	19		11	12	13	14	15	16	17	
17	18	19	20	21	22	23		21	22	23	24	25	26	27		18	19	20	21	22	23	24		16	17	18	19	20	21	22		20	21	22	23	24	25	26		18	19	20	21	22	23	24	
24	25	26	27	28	29	30		28	29	30	31					25	26	27	28	29	30			23	24	25	26	27	28	29		27	28	29	30					25	26	27	28	29	30	31	
31																							30	31																					

FEBRUARY
WEEK 07

13 MONDAY

THINGS TO DO/NOTES

14 TUESDAY

THINGS TO DO/NOTES

VALENTINE'S DAY

15 WEDNESDAY

THINGS TO DO/NOTES

JANUARY								FEBRUARY								MARCH								APRIL								MAY								JUNE						
M	T	W	T	F	S	S		M	T	W	T	F	S	S		M	T	W	T	F	S	S		M	T	W	T	F	S	S		M	T	W	T	F	S	S		M	T	W	T	F	S	S
						01				01	02	03	04	05				01	02	03	04	05						01	02		01	02	03	04	05	06	07				01	02	03	04
02	03	04	05	06	07	08		06	07	08	09	10	11	12		06	07	08	09	10	11	12		03	04	05	06	07	08	09		08	09	10	11	12	13	14		05	06	07	08	09	10	11
09	10	11	12	13	14	15		13	14	15	16	17	18	19		13	14	15	16	17	18	19		10	11	12	13	14	15	16		15	16	17	18	19	20	21		12	13	14	15	16	17	18
16	17	18	19	20	21	22		20	21	22	23	24	25	26		20	21	22	23	24	25	26		17	18	19	20	21	22	23		22	23	24	25	26	27	28		19	20	21	22	23	24	25
23	24	25	26	27	28	29		27	28							27	28	29	30	31				24	25	26	27	28	29	30		29	30	31						26	27	28	29	30		
30	31																																											

THURSDAY 16
THINGS TO DO/NOTES

FRIDAY 17
THINGS TO DO/NOTES

MAHA SHIVARATRI; ISRA AND MI'RAJ

SATURDAY 18
THINGS TO DO/NOTES

SUNDAY 19
THINGS TO DO/NOTES

	JULY							AUGUST							SEPTEMBER							OCTOBER							NOVEMBER							DECEMBER					
M	T	W	T	F	S	S	M	T	W	T	F	S	S	M	T	W	T	F	S	S	M	T	W	T	F	S	S	M	T	W	T	F	S	S	M	T	W	T	F	S	S
					01	02		01	02	03	04	05	06					01	02	03						01			01	02	03	04	05					01	02	03
03	04	05	06	07	08	09	07	08	09	10	11	12	13	04	05	06	07	08	09	10	02	03	04	05	06	07	08	06	07	08	09	10	11	12	04	05	06	07	08	09	10
10	11	12	13	14	15	16	14	15	16	17	18	19	20	11	12	13	14	15	16	17	09	10	11	12	13	14	15	13	14	15	16	17	18	19	11	12	13	14	15	16	17
17	18	19	20	21	22	23	21	22	23	24	25	26	27	18	19	20	21	22	23	24	16	17	18	19	20	21	22	20	21	22	23	24	25	26	18	19	20	21	22	23	24
24	25	26	27	28	29	30	28	29	30	31				25	26	27	28	29	30		23	24	25	26	27	28	29	27	28	29	30				25	26	27	28	29	30	31
31																					30	31																			

FEBRUARY
WEEK 08

20 MONDAY
PRESIDENTS' DAY (USA)

THINGS TO DO/NOTES

21 TUESDAY
SHROVE TUESDAY

THINGS TO DO/NOTES

22 WEDNESDAY
ASH WEDNESDAY

THINGS TO DO/NOTES

JANUARY	FEBRUARY	MARCH	APRIL	MAY	JUNE
M T W T F S S	M T W T F S S	M T W T F S S	M T W T F S S	M T W T F S S	M T W T F S S
01	01 02 03 04 05	01 02 03 04 05	01 02	01 02 03 04 05 06 07	01 02 03 04
02 03 04 05 06 07 08	06 07 08 09 10 11 12	06 07 08 09 10 11 12	03 04 05 06 07 08 09	08 09 10 11 12 13 14	05 06 07 08 09 10 11
09 10 11 12 13 14 15	13 14 15 16 17 18 19	13 14 15 16 17 18 19	10 11 12 13 14 15 16	15 16 17 18 19 20 21	12 13 14 15 16 17 18
16 17 18 19 20 21 22	20 21 22 23 24 25 26	20 21 22 23 24 25 26	17 18 19 20 21 22 23	22 23 24 25 26 27 28	19 20 21 22 23 24 25
23 24 25 26 27 28 29	27 28	27 28 29 30 31	24 25 26 27 28 29 30	29 30 31	26 27 28 29 30
30 31					

FEBRUARY
WEEK 08

THURSDAY 23
THINGS TO DO/NOTES

FRIDAY 24
THINGS TO DO/NOTES

SATURDAY 25
THINGS TO DO/NOTES

SUNDAY 26
THINGS TO DO/NOTES

JULY								AUGUST								SEPTEMBER								OCTOBER								NOVEMBER								DECEMBER						
M	T	W	T	F	S	S		M	T	W	T	F	S	S		M	T	W	T	F	S	S		M	T	W	T	F	S	S		M	T	W	T	F	S	S		M	T	W	T	F	S	S
					01	02			01	02	03	04	05	06						01	02	03						01			01	02	03	04	05						01	02	03
03	04	05	06	07	08	09		07	08	09	10	11	12	13		04	05	06	07	08	09	10		02	03	04	05	06	07	08		06	07	08	09	10	11	12		04	05	06	07	08	09	10
10	11	12	13	14	15	16		14	15	16	17	18	19	20		11	12	13	14	15	16	17		09	10	11	12	13	14	15		13	14	15	16	17	18	19		11	12	13	14	15	16	17
17	18	19	20	21	22	23		21	22	23	24	25	26	27		18	19	20	21	22	23	24		16	17	18	19	20	21	22		20	21	22	23	24	25	26		18	19	20	21	22	23	24
24	25	26	27	28	29	30		28	29	30	31					25	26	27	28	29	30			23	24	25	26	27	28	29		27	28	29	30					25	26	27	28	29	30	31
31																							30	31																				

FEBRUARY
WEEK 09

MARCH

27 MONDAY
THINGS TO DO/NOTES

28 TUESDAY
THINGS TO DO/NOTES

01 WEDNESDAY
THINGS TO DO/NOTES

ST DAVID'S DAY (WALES)

JANUARY	FEBRUARY	MARCH	APRIL	MAY	JUNE
M T W T F S S	M T W T F S S	M T W T F S S	M T W T F S S	M T W T F S S	M T W T F S S

JANUARY
M T W T F S S
01
02 03 04 05 06 07 08
09 10 11 12 13 14 15
16 17 18 19 20 21 22
23 24 25 26 27 28 29
30 31

FEBRUARY
M T W T F S S
01 02 03 04 05
06 07 08 09 10 11 12
13 14 15 16 17 18 19
20 21 22 23 24 25 26
27 28

MARCH
M T W T F S S
01 02 03 04 05
06 07 08 09 10 11 12
13 14 15 16 17 18 19
20 21 22 23 24 25 26
27 28 29 30 31

APRIL
M T W T F S S
01 02
03 04 05 06 07 08 09
10 11 12 13 14 15 16
17 18 19 20 21 22 23
24 25 26 27 28 29 30

MAY
M T W T F S S
01 02 03 04 05 06 07
08 09 10 11 12 13 14
15 16 17 18 19 20 21
22 23 24 25 26 27 28
29 30 31

JUNE
M T W T F S S
01 02 03 04
05 06 07 08 09 10 11
12 13 14 15 16 17 18
19 20 21 22 23 24 25
26 27 28 29 30

THURSDAY 02

THINGS TO DO/NOTES

FRIDAY 03

THINGS TO DO/NOTES

SATURDAY 04

THINGS TO DO/NOTES

SUNDAY 05

THINGS TO DO/NOTES

JULY								AUGUST								SEPTEMBER								OCTOBER								NOVEMBER								DECEMBER						
M	T	W	T	F	S	S		M	T	W	T	F	S	S		M	T	W	T	F	S	S		M	T	W	T	F	S	S		M	T	W	T	F	S	S		M	T	W	T	F	S	S
				01	02			01	02	03	04	05	06						01	02	03							01			01	02	03	04	05						01	02	03
03	04	05	06	07	08	09		07	08	09	10	11	12	13		04	05	06	07	08	09	10		02	03	04	05	06	07	08		06	07	08	09	10	11	12		04	05	06	07	08	09	10
10	11	12	13	14	15	16		14	15	16	17	18	19	20		11	12	13	14	15	16	17		09	10	11	12	13	14	15		13	14	15	16	17	18	19		11	12	13	14	15	16	17
17	18	19	20	21	22	23		21	22	23	24	25	26	27		18	19	20	21	22	23	24		16	17	18	19	20	21	22		20	21	22	23	24	25	26		18	19	20	21	22	23	24
24	25	26	27	28	29	30		28	29	30	31					25	26	27	28	29	30			23	24	25	26	27	28	29		27	28	29	30					25	26	27	28	29	30	31
31																							30	31																				

MARCH
WEEK 10

06 MONDAY
THINGS TO DO/NOTES

07 TUESDAY
THINGS TO DO/NOTES

PURIM

08 WEDNESDAY
THINGS TO DO/NOTES

HOLI

JANUARY								FEBRUARY								MARCH								APRIL								MAY								JUNE						
M	T	W	T	F	S	S		M	T	W	T	F	S	S		M	T	W	T	F	S	S		M	T	W	T	F	S	S		M	T	W	T	F	S	S		M	T	W	T	F	S	S
						01				01	02	03	04	05				01	02	03	04	05						01	02		01	02	03	04	05	06	07					01	02	03	04
02	03	04	05	06	07	08		06	07	08	09	10	11	12		06	07	08	09	10	11	12		03	04	05	06	07	08	09		08	09	10	11	12	13	14		05	06	07	08	09	10	11
09	10	11	12	13	14	15		13	14	15	16	17	18	19		13	14	15	16	17	18	19		10	11	12	13	14	15	16		15	16	17	18	19	20	21		12	13	14	15	16	17	18
16	17	18	19	20	21	22		20	21	22	23	24	25	26		20	21	22	23	24	25	26		17	18	19	20	21	22	23		22	23	24	25	26	27	28		19	20	21	22	23	24	25
23	24	25	26	27	28	29		27	28							27	28	29	30	31				24	25	26	27	28	29	30		29	30	31						26	27	28	29	30		
30	31																																											

MARCH
WEEK 10

THURSDAY 09
THINGS TO DO/NOTES

FRIDAY 10
THINGS TO DO/NOTES

SATURDAY 11
THINGS TO DO/NOTES

SUNDAY 12
THINGS TO DO/NOTES

JULY							AUGUST							SEPTEMBER							OCTOBER							NOVEMBER							DECEMBER						
M	T	W	T	F	S	S	M	T	W	T	F	S	S	M	T	W	T	F	S	S	M	T	W	T	F	S	S	M	T	W	T	F	S	S	M	T	W	T	F	S	S
				01	02			01	02	03	04	05	06					01	02	03						01			01	02	03	04	05				01	02	03
03	04	05	06	07	08	09	07	08	09	10	11	12	13	04	05	06	07	08	09	10	02	03	04	05	06	07	08	06	07	08	09	10	11	12	04	05	06	07	08	09	10
10	11	12	13	14	15	16	14	15	16	17	18	19	20	11	12	13	14	15	16	17	09	10	11	12	13	14	15	13	14	15	16	17	18	19	11	12	13	14	15	16	17
17	18	19	20	21	22	23	21	22	23	24	25	26	27	18	19	20	21	22	23	24	16	17	18	19	20	21	22	20	21	22	23	24	25	26	18	19	20	21	22	23	24
24	25	26	27	28	29	30	28	29	30	31				25	26	27	28	29	30		23	24	25	26	27	28	29	27	28	29	30				25	26	27	28	29	30	31
31																					30	31																			

MARCH
WEEK II

13 MONDAY
THINGS TO DO/NOTES

14 TUESDAY
THINGS TO DO/NOTES

15 WEDNESDAY
THINGS TO DO/NOTES

JANUARY	FEBRUARY	MARCH	APRIL	MAY	JUNE
M T W T F S S	M T W T F S S	M T W T F S S	M T W T F S S	M T W T F S S	M T W T F S S
01	01 02 03 04 05	01 02 03 04 05	01 02	01 02 03 04 05 06 07	01 02 03 04
02 03 04 05 06 07 08	06 07 08 09 10 11 12	06 07 08 09 10 11 12	03 04 05 06 07 08 09	08 09 10 11 12 13 14	05 06 07 08 09 10 11
09 10 11 12 13 14 15	13 14 15 16 17 18 19	13 14 15 16 17 18 19	10 11 12 13 14 15 16	15 16 17 18 19 20 21	12 13 14 15 16 17 18
16 17 18 19 20 21 22	20 21 22 23 24 25 26	20 21 22 23 24 25 26	17 18 19 20 21 22 23	22 23 24 25 26 27 28	19 20 21 22 23 24 25
23 24 25 26 27 28 29	27 28	27 28 29 30 31	24 25 26 27 28 29 30	29 30 31	26 27 28 29 30
30 31					

MARCH
WEEK II

THURSDAY 16

THINGS TO DO/NOTES

ST PATRICK'S DAY (N. IRELAND & ROI)

FRIDAY 17

THINGS TO DO/NOTES

SATURDAY 18

THINGS TO DO/NOTES

MOTHER'S DAY

SUNDAY 19

THINGS TO DO/NOTES

JULY								AUGUST								SEPTEMBER								OCTOBER								NOVEMBER								DECEMBER						
M	T	W	T	F	S	S		M	T	W	T	F	S	S		M	T	W	T	F	S	S		M	T	W	T	F	S	S		M	T	W	T	F	S	S		M	T	W	T	F	S	S
					01	02				01	02	03	04	05	06					01	02	03							01				01	02	03	04	05						01	02	03
03	04	05	06	07	08	09		07	08	09	10	11	12	13		04	05	06	07	08	09	10		02	03	04	05	06	07	08		06	07	08	09	10	11	12		04	05	06	07	08	09	10
10	11	12	13	14	15	16		14	15	16	17	18	19	20		11	12	13	14	15	16	17		09	10	11	12	13	14	15		13	14	15	16	17	18	19		11	12	13	14	15	16	17
17	18	19	20	21	22	23		21	22	23	24	25	26	27		18	19	20	21	22	23	24		16	17	18	19	20	21	22		20	21	22	23	24	25	26		18	19	20	21	22	23	24
24	25	26	27	28	29	30		28	29	30	31					25	26	27	28	29	30			23	24	25	26	27	28	29		27	28	29	30					25	26	27	28	29	30	31
31																							30	31																				

MARCH

20 MONDAY
THINGS TO DO/NOTES

VERNAL EQUINOX

21 TUESDAY
THINGS TO DO/NOTES

22 WEDNESDAY
THINGS TO DO/NOTES

RAMADAN STARTS

JANUARY						
M	T	W	T	F	S	S
						01
02	03	04	05	06	07	08
09	10	11	12	13	14	15
16	17	18	19	20	21	22
23	24	25	26	27	28	29
30	31					

FEBRUARY						
M	T	W	T	F	S	S
		01	02	03	04	05
06	07	08	09	10	11	12
13	14	15	16	17	18	19
20	21	22	23	24	25	26
27	28					

MARCH						
M	T	W	T	F	S	S
		01	02	03	04	05
06	07	08	09	10	11	12
13	14	15	16	17	18	19
20	21	22	23	24	25	26
27	28	29	30	31		

APRIL						
M	T	W	T	F	S	S
					01	02
03	04	05	06	07	08	09
10	11	12	13	14	15	16
17	18	19	20	21	22	23
24	25	26	27	28	29	30

MAY						
M	T	W	T	F	S	S
01	02	03	04	05	06	07
08	09	10	11	12	13	14
15	16	17	18	19	20	21
22	23	24	25	26	27	28
29	30	31				

JUNE						
M	T	W	T	F	S	S
			01	02	03	04
05	06	07	08	09	10	11
12	13	14	15	16	17	18
19	20	21	22	23	24	25
26	27	28	29	30		

MARCH
WEEK 12

THURSDAY 23
THINGS TO DO/NOTES

FRIDAY 24
THINGS TO DO/NOTES

SATURDAY 25
THINGS TO DO/NOTES

BRITISH SUMMER TIME BEGINS

SUNDAY 26
THINGS TO DO/NOTES

JULY								AUGUST								SEPTEMBER								OCTOBER								NOVEMBER								DECEMBER						
M	T	W	T	F	S	S		M	T	W	T	F	S	S		M	T	W	T	F	S	S		M	T	W	T	F	S	S		M	T	W	T	F	S	S		M	T	W	T	F	S	S
				01	02			01	02	03	04	05	06						01	02	03							01		01	02	03	04	05					01	02	03
03	04	05	06	07	08	09		07	08	09	10	11	12	13		04	05	06	07	08	09	10		02	03	04	05	06	07	08		06	07	08	09	10	11	12		04	05	06	07	08	09	10
10	11	12	13	14	15	16		14	15	16	17	18	19	20		11	12	13	14	15	16	17		09	10	11	12	13	14	15		13	14	15	16	17	18	19		11	12	13	14	15	16	17
17	18	19	20	21	22	23		21	22	23	24	25	26	27		18	19	20	21	22	23	24		16	17	18	19	20	21	22		20	21	22	23	24	25	26		18	19	20	21	22	23	24
24	25	26	27	28	29	30		28	29	30	31					25	26	27	28	29	30			23	24	25	26	27	28	29		27	28	29	30					25	26	27	28	29	30	31
31																							30	31																			

MARCH
WEEK 13

27 MONDAY
THINGS TO DO/NOTES

28 TUESDAY
THINGS TO DO/NOTES

29 WEDNESDAY
THINGS TO DO/NOTES

JANUARY						
M	T	W	T	F	S	S
						01
02	03	04	05	06	07	08
09	10	11	12	13	14	15
16	17	18	19	20	21	22
23	24	25	26	27	28	29
30	31					

FEBRUARY						
M	T	W	T	F	S	S
		01	02	03	04	05
06	07	08	09	10	11	12
13	14	15	16	17	18	19
20	21	22	23	24	25	26
27	28					

MARCH						
M	T	W	T	F	S	S
		01	02	03	04	05
06	07	08	09	10	11	12
13	14	15	16	17	18	19
20	21	22	23	24	25	26
27	28	29	30	31		

APRIL						
M	T	W	T	F	S	S
					01	02
03	04	05	06	07	08	09
10	11	12	13	14	15	16
17	18	19	20	21	22	23
24	25	26	27	28	29	30

MAY						
M	T	W	T	F	S	S
01	02	03	04	05	06	07
08	09	10	11	12	13	14
15	16	17	18	19	20	21
22	23	24	25	26	27	28
29	30	31				

JUNE						
M	T	W	T	F	S	S
			01	02	03	04
05	06	07	08	09	10	11
12	13	14	15	16	17	18
19	20	21	22	23	24	25
26	27	28	29	30		

RAMA NAVAMI

THURSDAY **30**

THINGS TO DO/NOTES

FRIDAY **31**

THINGS TO DO/NOTES

SATURDAY **01**

THINGS TO DO/NOTES

PALM SUNDAY

SUNDAY **02**

THINGS TO DO/NOTES

JULY							AUGUST							SEPTEMBER							OCTOBER							NOVEMBER							DECEMBER						
M	T	W	T	F	S	S	M	T	W	T	F	S	S	M	T	W	T	F	S	S	M	T	W	T	F	S	S	M	T	W	T	F	S	S	M	T	W	T	F	S	S
					01	02			01	02	03	04	05	06					01	02	03					01				01	02	03	04	05				01	02	03
03	04	05	06	07	08	09	07	08	09	10	11	12	13	04	05	06	07	08	09	10	02	03	04	05	06	07	08	06	07	08	09	10	11	12	04	05	06	07	08	09	10
10	11	12	13	14	15	16	14	15	16	17	18	19	20	11	12	13	14	15	16	17	09	10	11	12	13	14	15	13	14	15	16	17	18	19	11	12	13	14	15	16	17
17	18	19	20	21	22	23	21	22	23	24	25	26	27	18	19	20	21	22	23	24	16	17	18	19	20	21	22	20	21	22	23	24	25	26	18	19	20	21	22	23	24
24	25	26	27	28	29	30	28	29	30	31				25	26	27	28	29	30		23	24	25	26	27	28	29	27	28	29	30				25	26	27	28	29	30	31
31																					30	31																			

APRIL
WEEK 14

03 MONDAY
THINGS TO DO/NOTES

04 TUESDAY
THINGS TO DO/NOTES

05 WEDNESDAY
THINGS TO DO/NOTES

JANUARY								FEBRUARY								MARCH								APRIL								MAY								JUNE						
M	T	W	T	F	S	S		M	T	W	T	F	S	S		M	T	W	T	F	S	S		M	T	W	T	F	S	S		M	T	W	T	F	S	S		M	T	W	T	F	S	S
					01	02				01	02	03	04	05				01	02	03	04	05							01	02		01	02	03	04	05	06	07					01	02	03	04
02	03	04	05	06	07	08		06	07	08	09	10	11	12		06	07	08	09	10	11	12		03	04	05	06	07	08	09		08	09	10	11	12	13	14		05	06	07	08	09	10	11
09	10	11	12	13	14	15		13	14	15	16	17	18	19		13	14	15	16	17	18	19		10	11	12	13	14	15	16		15	16	17	18	19	20	21		12	13	14	15	16	17	18
16	17	18	19	20	21	22		20	21	22	23	24	25	26		20	21	22	23	24	25	26		17	18	19	20	21	22	23		22	23	24	25	26	27	28		19	20	21	22	23	24	25
23	24	25	26	27	28	29		27	28							27	28	29	30	31				24	25	26	27	28	29	30		29	30	31						26	27	28	29	30		
30	31																																											

APRIL
WEEK 14

MAUNDY THURSDAY; FIRST DAY OF PASSOVER

THURSDAY 06

THINGS TO DO/NOTES

GOOD FRIDAY

FRIDAY 07

THINGS TO DO/NOTES

HOLY SATURDAY

SATURDAY 08

THINGS TO DO/NOTES

EASTER SUNDAY

SUNDAY 09

THINGS TO DO/NOTES

JULY						
M	T	W	T	F	S	S
					01	02
03	04	05	06	07	08	09
10	11	12	13	14	15	16
17	18	19	20	21	22	23
24	25	26	27	28	29	30
31						

AUGUST						
M	T	W	T	F	S	S
	01	02	03	04	05	06
07	08	09	10	11	12	13
14	15	16	17	18	19	20
21	22	23	24	25	26	27
28	29	30	31			

SEPTEMBER						
M	T	W	T	F	S	S
				01	02	03
04	05	06	07	08	09	10
11	12	13	14	15	16	17
18	19	20	21	22	23	24
25	26	27	28	29	30	

OCTOBER						
M	T	W	T	F	S	S
						01
02	03	04	05	06	07	08
09	10	11	12	13	14	15
16	17	18	19	20	21	22
23	24	25	26	27	28	29
30	31					

NOVEMBER						
M	T	W	T	F	S	S
		01	02	03	04	05
06	07	08	09	10	11	12
13	14	15	16	17	18	19
20	21	22	23	24	25	26
27	28	29	30			

DECEMBER						
M	T	W	T	F	S	S
				01	02	03
04	05	06	07	08	09	10
11	12	13	14	15	16	17
18	19	20	21	22	23	24
25	26	27	28	29	30	31

APRIL
WEEK 15

10 MONDAY

EASTER MONDAY (UK, ROI, CAN, AUS, NZ)

THINGS TO DO/NOTES

11 TUESDAY

THINGS TO DO/NOTES

12 WEDNESDAY

THINGS TO DO/NOTES

JANUARY	FEBRUARY	MARCH	APRIL	MAY	JUNE
M T W T F S S	M T W T F S S	M T W T F S S	M T W T F S S	M T W T F S S	M T W T F S S
01	01 02 03 04 05	01 02 03 04 05	01 02	01 02 03 04 05 06 07	01 02 03 04
02 03 04 05 06 07 08	06 07 08 09 10 11 12	06 07 08 09 10 11 12	03 04 05 06 07 08 09	08 09 10 11 12 13 14	05 06 07 08 09 10 11
09 10 11 12 13 14 15	13 14 15 16 17 18 19	13 14 15 16 17 18 19	10 11 12 13 14 15 16	15 16 17 18 19 20 21	12 13 14 15 16 17 18
16 17 18 19 20 21 22	20 21 22 23 24 25 26	20 21 22 23 24 25 26	17 18 19 20 21 22 23	22 23 24 25 26 27 28	19 20 21 22 23 24 25
23 24 25 26 27 28 29	27 28	27 28 29 30 31	24 25 26 27 28 29 30	29 30 31	26 27 28 29 30
30 31					

LAST DAY OF PASSOVER

THURSDAY 13
THINGS TO DO/NOTES

FRIDAY 14
THINGS TO DO/NOTES

SATURDAY 15
THINGS TO DO/NOTES

SUNDAY 16
THINGS TO DO/NOTES

JULY	AUGUST	SEPTEMBER	OCTOBER	NOVEMBER	DECEMBER
M T W T F S S	M T W T F S S	M T W T F S S	M T W T F S S	M T W T F S S	M T W T F S S
01 02	01 02 03 04 05 06	01 02 03	01	01 02 03 04 05	01 02 03
03 04 05 06 07 08 09	07 08 09 10 11 12 13	04 05 06 07 08 09 10	02 03 04 05 06 07 08	06 07 08 09 10 11 12	04 05 06 07 08 09 10
10 11 12 13 14 15 16	14 15 16 17 18 19 20	11 12 13 14 15 16 17	09 10 11 12 13 14 15	13 14 15 16 17 18 19	11 12 13 14 15 16 17
17 18 19 20 21 22 23	21 22 23 24 25 26 27	18 19 20 21 22 23 24	16 17 18 19 20 21 22	20 21 22 23 24 25 26	18 19 20 21 22 23 24
24 25 26 27 28 29 30	28 29 30 31	25 26 27 28 29 30	23 24 25 26 27 28 29	27 28 29 30	25 26 27 28 29 30 31
31			30 31		

APRIL

17 MONDAY
THINGS TO DO/NOTES

18 TUESDAY
THINGS TO DO/NOTES

YOM HASHOAH; LAYLATUL QADR (NIGHT OF POWER)

19 WEDNESDAY
THINGS TO DO/NOTES

JANUARY								FEBRUARY								MARCH								APRIL								MAY								JUNE						
M	T	W	T	F	S	S		M	T	W	T	F	S	S		M	T	W	T	F	S	S		M	T	W	T	F	S	S		M	T	W	T	F	S	S		M	T	W	T	F	S	S
						01				01	02	03	04	05				01	02	03	04	05						01	02		01	02	03	04	05	06	07					01	02	03	04
02	03	04	05	06	07	08		06	07	08	09	10	11	12		06	07	08	09	10	11	12		03	04	05	06	07	08	09		08	09	10	11	12	13	14		05	06	07	08	09	10	11
09	10	11	12	13	14	15		13	14	15	16	17	18	19		13	14	15	16	17	18	19		10	11	12	13	14	15	16		15	16	17	18	19	20	21		12	13	14	15	16	17	18
16	17	18	19	20	21	22		20	21	22	23	24	25	26		20	21	22	23	24	25	26		17	18	19	20	21	22	23		22	23	24	25	26	27	28		19	20	21	22	23	24	25
23	24	25	26	27	28	29		27	28							27	28	29	30	31				24	25	26	27	28	29	30		29	30	31						26	27	28	29	30		
30	31																																											

THURSDAY 20
THINGS TO DO/NOTES

FRIDAY 21
THINGS TO DO/NOTES

EID AL-FITR

SATURDAY 22
THINGS TO DO/NOTES

ST GEORGE'S DAY; SHAKESPEARE DAY

SUNDAY 23
THINGS TO DO/NOTES

JULY							AUGUST							SEPTEMBER							OCTOBER							NOVEMBER							DECEMBER						
M	T	W	T	F	S	S	M	T	W	T	F	S	S	M	T	W	T	F	S	S	M	T	W	T	F	S	S	M	T	W	T	F	S	S	M	T	W	T	F	S	S
					01	02		01	02	03	04	05	06					01	02	03							01			01	02	03	04	05					01	02	03
03	04	05	06	07	08	09	07	08	09	10	11	12	13	04	05	06	07	08	09	10	02	03	04	05	06	07	08	06	07	08	09	10	11	12	04	05	06	07	08	09	10
10	11	12	13	14	15	16	14	15	16	17	18	19	20	11	12	13	14	15	16	17	09	10	11	12	13	14	15	13	14	15	16	17	18	19	11	12	13	14	15	16	17
17	18	19	20	21	22	23	21	22	23	24	25	26	27	18	19	20	21	22	23	24	16	17	18	19	20	21	22	20	21	22	23	24	25	26	18	19	20	21	22	23	24
24	25	26	27	28	29	30	28	29	30	31				25	26	27	28	29	30		23	24	25	26	27	28	29	27	28	29	30				25	26	27	28	29	30	31
31																					30	31																			

APRIL
WEEK 17

24 MONDAY
THINGS TO DO/NOTES

25 TUESDAY
THINGS TO DO/NOTES

ANZAC DAY (AUS, NZ)

26 WEDNESDAY
THINGS TO DO/NOTES

YOM HAATZMAUT

JANUARY	FEBRUARY	MARCH	APRIL	MAY	JUNE
M T W T F S S	M T W T F S S	M T W T F S S	M T W T F S S	M T W T F S S	M T W T F S S
01	01 02 03 04 05	01 02 03 04 05	01 02	01 02 03 04 05 06 07	01 02 03 04
02 03 04 05 06 07 08	06 07 08 09 10 11 12	06 07 08 09 10 11 12	03 04 05 06 07 08 09	08 09 10 11 12 13 14	05 06 07 08 09 10 11
09 10 11 12 13 14 15	13 14 15 16 17 18 19	13 14 15 16 17 18 19	10 11 12 13 14 15 16	15 16 17 18 19 20 21	12 13 14 15 16 17 18
16 17 18 19 20 21 22	20 21 22 23 24 25 26	20 21 22 23 24 25 26	17 18 19 20 21 22 23	22 23 24 25 26 27 28	19 20 21 22 23 24 25
23 24 25 26 27 28 29	27 28	27 28 29 30 31	24 25 26 27 28 29 30	29 30 31	26 27 28 29 30
30 31					

THURSDAY 27
THINGS TO DO/NOTES

FRIDAY 28
THINGS TO DO/NOTES

SATURDAY 29
THINGS TO DO/NOTES

SUNDAY 30
THINGS TO DO/NOTES

JULY								AUGUST								SEPTEMBER								OCTOBER								NOVEMBER								DECEMBER						
M	T	W	T	F	S	S		M	T	W	T	F	S	S		M	T	W	T	F	S	S		M	T	W	T	F	S	S		M	T	W	T	F	S	S		M	T	W	T	F	S	S
					01	02			01	02	03	04	05	06						01	02	03							01				01	02	03	04	05						01	02	03
03	04	05	06	07	08	09		07	08	09	10	11	12	13		04	05	06	07	08	09	10		02	03	04	05	06	07	08		06	07	08	09	10	11	12		04	05	06	07	08	09	10
10	11	12	13	14	15	16		14	15	16	17	18	19	20		11	12	13	14	15	16	17		09	10	11	12	13	14	15		13	14	15	16	17	18	19		11	12	13	14	15	16	17
17	18	19	20	21	22	23		21	22	23	24	25	26	27		18	19	20	21	22	23	24		16	17	18	19	20	21	22		20	21	22	23	24	25	26		18	19	20	21	22	23	24
24	25	26	27	28	29	30		28	29	30	31					25	26	27	28	29	30			23	24	25	26	27	28	29		27	28	29	30					25	26	27	28	29	30	31
31																							30	31																				

MAY
WEEK 18

01 MONDAY
MAY BANK HOLIDAY (UK & ROI)

THINGS TO DO/NOTES

02 TUESDAY
THINGS TO DO/NOTES

03 WEDNESDAY
THINGS TO DO/NOTES

JANUARY	FEBRUARY	MARCH	APRIL	MAY	JUNE
M T W T F S S	M T W T F S S	M T W T F S S	M T W T F S S	M T W T F S S	M T W T F S S
01	01 02 03 04 05	01 02 03 04 05	01 02	01 02 03 04 05 06 07	01 02 03 04
02 03 04 05 06 07 08	06 07 08 09 10 11 12	06 07 08 09 10 11 12	03 04 05 06 07 08 09	08 09 10 11 12 13 14	05 06 07 08 09 10 11
09 10 11 12 13 14 15	13 14 15 16 17 18 19	13 14 15 16 17 18 19	10 11 12 13 14 15 16	15 16 17 18 19 20 21	12 13 14 15 16 17 18
16 17 18 19 20 21 22	20 21 22 23 24 25 26	20 21 22 23 24 25 26	17 18 19 20 21 22 23	22 23 24 25 26 27 28	19 20 21 22 23 24 25
23 24 25 26 27 28 29	27 28	27 28 29 30 31	24 25 26 27 28 29 30	29 30 31	26 27 28 29 30
30 31					

MAY
WEEK 18

THURSDAY 04
THINGS TO DO/NOTES

FRIDAY 05
THINGS TO DO/NOTES

SATURDAY 06
THINGS TO DO/NOTES

SUNDAY 07
THINGS TO DO/NOTES

JULY						
M	T	W	T	F	S	S
					01	02
03	04	05	06	07	08	09
10	11	12	13	14	15	16
17	18	19	20	21	22	23
24	25	26	27	28	29	30
31						

AUGUST						
M	T	W	T	F	S	S
	01	02	03	04	05	06
07	08	09	10	11	12	13
14	15	16	17	18	19	20
21	22	23	24	25	26	27
28	29	30	31			

SEPTEMBER						
M	T	W	T	F	S	S
			01	02	03	
04	05	06	07	08	09	10
11	12	13	14	15	16	17
18	19	20	21	22	23	24
25	26	27	28	29	30	

OCTOBER						
M	T	W	T	F	S	S
						01
02	03	04	05	06	07	08
09	10	11	12	13	14	15
16	17	18	19	20	21	22
23	24	25	26	27	28	29
30	31					

NOVEMBER						
M	T	W	T	F	S	S
		01	02	03	04	05
06	07	08	09	10	11	12
13	14	15	16	17	18	19
20	21	22	23	24	25	26
27	28	29	30			

DECEMBER						
M	T	W	T	F	S	S
				01	02	03
04	05	06	07	08	09	10
11	12	13	14	15	16	17
18	19	20	21	22	23	24
25	26	27	28	29	30	31

MAY

08 MONDAY

THINGS TO DO/NOTES

09 TUESDAY

THINGS TO DO/NOTES

LAG B'OMER

10 WEDNESDAY

THINGS TO DO/NOTES

JANUARY	FEBRUARY	MARCH	APRIL	MAY	JUNE
M T W T F S S	M T W T F S S	M T W T F S S	M T W T F S S	M T W T F S S	M T W T F S S
01	01 02 03 04 05	01 02 03 04 05	01 02	01 02 03 04 05 06 07	01 02 03 04
02 03 04 05 06 07 08	06 07 08 09 10 11 12	06 07 08 09 10 11 12	03 04 05 06 07 08 09	08 09 10 11 12 13 14	05 06 07 08 09 10 11
09 10 11 12 13 14 15	13 14 15 16 17 18 19	13 14 15 16 17 18 19	10 11 12 13 14 15 16	15 16 17 18 19 20 21	12 13 14 15 16 17 18
16 17 18 19 20 21 22	20 21 22 23 24 25 26	20 21 22 23 24 25 26	17 18 19 20 21 22 23	22 23 24 25 26 27 28	19 20 21 22 23 24 25
23 24 25 26 27 28 29	27 28	27 28 29 30 31	24 25 26 27 28 29 30	29 30 31	26 27 28 29 30
30 31					

MAY
WEEK 19

THURSDAY   11
THINGS TO DO/NOTES

FRIDAY   12
THINGS TO DO/NOTES

SATURDAY   13
THINGS TO DO/NOTES

SUNDAY   14
THINGS TO DO/NOTES

JULY							AUGUST							SEPTEMBER							OCTOBER							NOVEMBER							DECEMBER						
M	T	W	T	F	S	S	M	T	W	T	F	S	S	M	T	W	T	F	S	S	M	T	W	T	F	S	S	M	T	W	T	F	S	S	M	T	W	T	F	S	S
					01	02			01	02	03	04	05	06					01	02	03							01		01	02	03	04	05					01	02	03
03	04	05	06	07	08	09	07	08	09	10	11	12	13	04	05	06	07	08	09	10	02	03	04	05	06	07	08	06	07	08	09	10	11	12	04	05	06	07	08	09	10
10	11	12	13	14	15	16	14	15	16	17	18	19	20	11	12	13	14	15	16	17	09	10	11	12	13	14	15	13	14	15	16	17	18	19	11	12	13	14	15	16	17
17	18	19	20	21	22	23	21	22	23	24	25	26	27	18	19	20	21	22	23	24	16	17	18	19	20	21	22	20	21	22	23	24	25	26	18	19	20	21	22	23	24
24	25	26	27	28	29	30	28	29	30	31				25	26	27	28	29	30		23	24	25	26	27	28	29	27	28	29	30				25	26	27	28	29	30	31
31																					30	31																		

MAY
WEEK 20

15 MONDAY
THINGS TO DO/NOTES

16 TUESDAY
THINGS TO DO/NOTES

17 WEDNESDAY
THINGS TO DO/NOTES

JANUARY	FEBRUARY	MARCH	APRIL	MAY	JUNE
M T W T F S S	M T W T F S S	M T W T F S S	M T W T F S S	M T W T F S S	M T W T F S S
01	01 02 03 04 05	01 02 03 04 05	01 02	01 02 03 04 05 06 07	01 02 03 04
02 03 04 05 06 07 08	06 07 08 09 10 11 12	06 07 08 09 10 11 12	03 04 05 06 07 08 09	08 09 10 11 12 13 14	05 06 07 08 09 10 11
09 10 11 12 13 14 15	13 14 15 16 17 18 19	13 14 15 16 17 18 19	10 11 12 13 14 15 16	15 16 17 18 19 20 21	12 13 14 15 16 17 18
16 17 18 19 20 21 22	20 21 22 23 24 25 26	20 21 22 23 24 25 26	17 18 19 20 21 22 23	22 23 24 25 26 27 28	19 20 21 22 23 24 25
23 24 25 26 27 28 29	27 28	27 28 29 30 31	24 25 26 27 28 29 30	29 30 31	26 27 28 29 30
30 31					

MAY

ASCENSION DAY

THURSDAY 18
THINGS TO DO/NOTES

FRIDAY 19
THINGS TO DO/NOTES

SATURDAY 20
THINGS TO DO/NOTES

SUNDAY 21
THINGS TO DO/NOTES

	JULY							AUGUST							SEPTEMBER							OCTOBER							NOVEMBER							DECEMBER					
M	T	W	T	F	S	S	M	T	W	T	F	S	S	M	T	W	T	F	S	S	M	T	W	T	F	S	S	M	T	W	T	F	S	S	M	T	W	T	F	S	S
					01	02			01	02	03	04	05	06					01	02	03						01			01	02	03	04	05					01	02	03
03	04	05	06	07	08	09	07	08	09	10	11	12	13	04	05	06	07	08	09	10	02	03	04	05	06	07	08	06	07	08	09	10	11	12	04	05	06	07	08	09	10
10	11	12	13	14	15	16	14	15	16	17	18	19	20	11	12	13	14	15	16	17	09	10	11	12	13	14	15	13	14	15	16	17	18	19	11	12	13	14	15	16	17
17	18	19	20	21	22	23	21	22	23	24	25	26	27	18	19	20	21	22	23	24	16	17	18	19	20	21	22	20	21	22	23	24	25	26	18	19	20	21	22	23	24
24	25	26	27	28	29	30	28	29	30	31				25	26	27	28	29	30		23	24	25	26	27	28	29	27	28	29	30				25	26	27	28	29	30	31
31																					30	31																			

MAY
WEEK 21

22 MONDAY
THINGS TO DO/NOTES

VICTORIA DAY (CAN)

23 TUESDAY
THINGS TO DO/NOTES

24 WEDNESDAY
THINGS TO DO/NOTES

JANUARY	FEBRUARY	MARCH	APRIL	MAY	JUNE
M T W T F S S	M T W T F S S	M T W T F S S	M T W T F S S	M T W T F S S	M T W T F S S
01	01 02 03 04 05	01 02 03 04 05	01 02	01 02 03 04 05 06 07	01 02 03 04
02 03 04 05 06 07 08	06 07 08 09 10 11 12	06 07 08 09 10 11 12	03 04 05 06 07 08 09	08 09 10 11 12 13 14	05 06 07 08 09 10 11
09 10 11 12 13 14 15	13 14 15 16 17 18 19	13 14 15 16 17 18 19	10 11 12 13 14 15 16	15 16 17 18 19 20 21	12 13 14 15 16 17 18
16 17 18 19 20 21 22	20 21 22 23 24 25 26	20 21 22 23 24 25 26	17 18 19 20 21 22 23	22 23 24 25 26 27 28	19 20 21 22 23 24 25
23 24 25 26 27 28 29	27 28	27 28 29 30 31	24 25 26 27 28 29 30	29 30 31	26 27 28 29 30
30 31					

MAY

THURSDAY 25
THINGS TO DO/NOTES

SHAVUOT

FRIDAY 26
THINGS TO DO/NOTES

SATURDAY 27
THINGS TO DO/NOTES

PENTECOST

SUNDAY 28
THINGS TO DO/NOTES

JULY	AUGUST	SEPTEMBER	OCTOBER	NOVEMBER	DECEMBER
M T W T F S S	M T W T F S S	M T W T F S S	M T W T F S S	M T W T F S S	M T W T F S S
01 02	01 02 03 04 05 06	01 02 03	01	01 02 03 04 05	01 02 03
03 04 05 06 07 08 09	07 08 09 10 11 12 13	04 05 06 07 08 09 10	02 03 04 05 06 07 08	06 07 08 09 10 11 12	04 05 06 07 08 09 10
10 11 12 13 14 15 16	14 15 16 17 18 19 20	11 12 13 14 15 16 17	09 10 11 12 13 14 15	13 14 15 16 17 18 19	11 12 13 14 15 16 17
17 18 19 20 21 22 23	21 22 23 24 25 26 27	18 19 20 21 22 23 24	16 17 18 19 20 21 22	20 21 22 23 24 25 26	18 19 20 21 22 23 24
24 25 26 27 28 29 30	28 29 30 31	25 26 27 28 29 30	23 24 25 26 27 28 29	27 28 29 30	25 26 27 28 29 30 31
31			30 31		

MAY

29 MONDAY
THINGS TO DO/NOTES

SPRING BANK HOLIDAY (UK); WHIT MONDAY; MEMORIAL DAY (USA)

30 TUESDAY
THINGS TO DO/NOTES

31 WEDNESDAY
THINGS TO DO/NOTES

JANUARY	FEBRUARY	MARCH	APRIL	MAY	JUNE
M T W T F S S	M T W T F S S	M T W T F S S	M T W T F S S	M T W T F S S	M T W T F S S
01	01 02 03 04 05	01 02 03 04 05	01 02	01 02 03 04 05 06 07	01 02 03 04
02 03 04 05 06 07 08	06 07 08 09 10 11 12	06 07 08 09 10 11 12	03 04 05 06 07 08 09	08 09 10 11 12 13 14	05 06 07 08 09 10 11
09 10 11 12 13 14 15	13 14 15 16 17 18 19	13 14 15 16 17 18 19	10 11 12 13 14 15 16	15 16 17 18 19 20 21	12 13 14 15 16 17 18
16 17 18 19 20 21 22	20 21 22 23 24 25 26	20 21 22 23 24 25 26	17 18 19 20 21 22 23	22 23 24 25 26 27 28	19 20 21 22 23 24 25
23 24 25 26 27 28 29	27 28	27 28 29 30 31	24 25 26 27 28 29 30	29 30 31	26 27 28 29 30
30 31					

JUNE
WEEK 22

THURSDAY 01
THINGS TO DO/NOTES

FRIDAY 02
THINGS TO DO/NOTES

SATURDAY 03
THINGS TO DO/NOTES

TRINITY SUNDAY

SUNDAY 04
THINGS TO DO/NOTES

JULY								AUGUST								SEPTEMBER								OCTOBER								NOVEMBER								DECEMBER						
M	T	W	T	F	S	S		M	T	W	T	F	S	S		M	T	W	T	F	S	S		M	T	W	T	F	S	S		M	T	W	T	F	S	S		M	T	W	T	F	S	S
				01	02			01	02	03	04	05	06					01	02	03							01			01	02	03	04	05						01	02	03
03	04	05	06	07	08	09		07	08	09	10	11	12	13		04	05	06	07	08	09	10		02	03	04	05	06	07	08		06	07	08	09	10	11	12		04	05	06	07	08	09	10
10	11	12	13	14	15	16		14	15	16	17	18	19	20		11	12	13	14	15	16	17		09	10	11	12	13	14	15		13	14	15	16	17	18	19		11	12	13	14	15	16	17
17	18	19	20	21	22	23		21	22	23	24	25	26	27		18	19	20	21	22	23	24		16	17	18	19	20	21	22		20	21	22	23	24	25	26		18	19	20	21	22	23	24
24	25	26	27	28	29	30		28	29	30	31					25	26	27	28	29	30			23	24	25	26	27	28	29		27	28	29	30					25	26	27	28	29	30	31
31																							30	31																				

JUNE
WEEK 23

05 MONDAY
THINGS TO DO/NOTES

JUNE BANK HOLIDAY (ROI); QUEEN'S BIRTHDAY (NZ)

06 TUESDAY
THINGS TO DO/NOTES

07 WEDNESDAY
THINGS TO DO/NOTES

JANUARY								FEBRUARY								MARCH								APRIL								MAY								JUNE						
M	T	W	T	F	S	S		M	T	W	T	F	S	S		M	T	W	T	F	S	S		M	T	W	T	F	S	S		M	T	W	T	F	S	S		M	T	W	T	F	S	S
						01					01	02	03	04	05		01	02	03	04	05						01	02							01	02							01	02	03	04
02	03	04	05	06	07	08		06	07	08	09	10	11	12		06	07	08	09	10	11	12		03	04	05	06	07	08	09		08	09	10	11	12	13	14		05	06	07	08	09	10	11
09	10	11	12	13	14	15		13	14	15	16	17	18	19		13	14	15	16	17	18	19		10	11	12	13	14	15	16		15	16	17	18	19	20	21		12	13	14	15	16	17	18
16	17	18	19	20	21	22		20	21	22	23	24	25	26		20	21	22	23	24	25	26		17	18	19	20	21	22	23		22	23	24	25	26	27	28		19	20	21	22	23	24	25
23	24	25	26	27	28	29		27	28							27	28	29	30	31				24	25	26	27	28	29	30		29	30	31						26	27	28	29	30		
30	31																																											

JUNE
WEEK 23

CORPUS CHRISTI

THURSDAY **08**
THINGS TO DO/NOTES

FRIDAY **09**
THINGS TO DO/NOTES

QUEEN'S OFFICIAL BIRTHDAY (UK)

SATURDAY **10**
THINGS TO DO/NOTES

SUNDAY **11**
THINGS TO DO/NOTES

JULY								AUGUST								SEPTEMBER								OCTOBER								NOVEMBER								DECEMBER						
M	T	W	T	F	S	S		M	T	W	T	F	S	S		M	T	W	T	F	S	S		M	T	W	T	F	S	S		M	T	W	T	F	S	S		M	T	W	T	F	S	S
				01	02			01	02	03	04	05	06		07				01	02	03							01		01	02	03	04	05						01	02	03
03	04	05	06	07	08	09		07	08	09	10	11	12	13		04	05	06	07	08	09	10		02	03	04	05	06	07	08		06	07	08	09	10	11	12		04	05	06	07	08	09	10
10	11	12	13	14	15	16		14	15	16	17	18	19	20		11	12	13	14	15	16	17		09	10	11	12	13	14	15		13	14	15	16	17	18	19		11	12	13	14	15	16	17
17	18	19	20	21	22	23		21	22	23	24	25	26	27		18	19	20	21	22	23	24		16	17	18	19	20	21	22		20	21	22	23	24	25	26		18	19	20	21	22	23	24
24	25	26	27	28	29	30		28	29	30	31					25	26	27	28	29	30			23	24	25	26	27	28	29		27	28	29	30					25	26	27	28	29	30	31
31																							30	31																				

JUNE
WEEK 24

12 MONDAY
THINGS TO DO/NOTES

13 TUESDAY
THINGS TO DO/NOTES

14 WEDNESDAY
THINGS TO DO/NOTES

JANUARY	FEBRUARY	MARCH	APRIL	MAY	JUNE
M T W T F S S	M T W T F S S	M T W T F S S	M T W T F S S	M T W T F S S	M T W T F S S
01	01 02 03 04 05	01 02 03 04 05	01 02	01 02 03 04 05 06 07	01 02 03 04
02 03 04 05 06 07 08	06 07 08 09 10 11 12	06 07 08 09 10 11 12	03 04 05 06 07 08 09	08 09 10 11 12 13 14	05 06 07 08 09 10 11
09 10 11 12 13 14 15	13 14 15 16 17 18 19	13 14 15 16 17 18 19	10 11 12 13 14 15 16	15 16 17 18 19 20 21	12 13 14 15 16 17 18
16 17 18 19 20 21 22	20 21 22 23 24 25 26	20 21 22 23 24 25 26	17 18 19 20 21 22 23	22 23 24 25 26 27 28	19 20 21 22 23 24 25
23 24 25 26 27 28 29	27 28	27 28 29 30 31	24 25 26 27 28 29 30	29 30 31	26 27 28 29 30
30 31					

JUNE
WEEK 24

THURSDAY 15
THINGS TO DO/NOTES

FRIDAY 16
THINGS TO DO/NOTES

SATURDAY 17
THINGS TO DO/NOTES

FATHER'S DAY

SUNDAY 18
THINGS TO DO/NOTES

JULY							
M	T	W	T	F	S	S	
				01	02		
03	04	05	06	07	08	09	
10	11	12	13	14	15	16	
17	18	19	20	21	22	23	
24	25	26	27	28	29	30	
31							

AUGUST						
M	T	W	T	F	S	S
01	02	03	04	05	06	
07	08	09	10	11	12	13
14	15	16	17	18	19	20
21	22	23	24	25	26	27
28	29	30	31			

SEPTEMBER						
M	T	W	T	F	S	S
				01	02	03
04	05	06	07	08	09	10
11	12	13	14	15	16	17
18	19	20	21	22	23	24
25	26	27	28	29	30	

OCTOBER						
M	T	W	T	F	S	S
						01
02	03	04	05	06	07	08
09	10	11	12	13	14	15
16	17	18	19	20	21	22
23	24	25	26	27	28	29
30	31					

NOVEMBER						
M	T	W	T	F	S	S
		01	02	03	04	05
06	07	08	09	10	11	12
13	14	15	16	17	18	19
20	21	22	23	24	25	26
27	28	29	30			

DECEMBER						
M	T	W	T	F	S	S
				01	02	03
04	05	06	07	08	09	10
11	12	13	14	15	16	17
18	19	20	21	22	23	24
25	26	27	28	29	30	31

JUNE
WEEK 25

19 MONDAY

THINGS TO DO/NOTES

20 TUESDAY

THINGS TO DO/NOTES

21 WEDNESDAY

THINGS TO DO/NOTES

SUMMER SOLSTICE

JANUARY								FEBRUARY								MARCH								APRIL								MAY								JUNE						
M	T	W	T	F	S	S		M	T	W	T	F	S	S		M	T	W	T	F	S	S		M	T	W	T	F	S	S		M	T	W	T	F	S	S		M	T	W	T	F	S	S
						01				01	02	03	04	05				01	02	03	04	05							01	02		01	02	03	04	05	06	07				01	02	03	04
02	03	04	05	06	07	08		06	07	08	09	10	11	12		06	07	08	09	10	11	12		03	04	05	06	07	08	09		08	09	10	11	12	13	14		05	06	07	08	09	10	11
09	10	11	12	13	14	15		13	14	15	16	17	18	19		13	14	15	16	17	18	19		10	11	12	13	14	15	16		15	16	17	18	19	20	21		12	13	14	15	16	17	18
16	17	18	19	20	21	22		20	21	22	23	24	25	26		20	21	22	23	24	25	26		17	18	19	20	21	22	23		22	23	24	25	26	27	28		19	20	21	22	23	24	25
23	24	25	26	27	28	29		27	28							27	28	29	30	31				24	25	26	27	28	29	30		29	30	31						26	27	28	29	30	
30	31																																												

WINDRUSH DAY

THURSDAY 22
THINGS TO DO/NOTES

FRIDAY 23
THINGS TO DO/NOTES

ARMED FORCES DAY (UK)

SATURDAY 24
THINGS TO DO/NOTES

SUNDAY 25
THINGS TO DO/NOTES

JULY							AUGUST							SEPTEMBER							OCTOBER							NOVEMBER							DECEMBER						
M	T	W	T	F	S	S	M	T	W	T	F	S	S	M	T	W	T	F	S	S	M	T	W	T	F	S	S	M	T	W	T	F	S	S	M	T	W	T	F	S	S
					01	02		01	02	03	04	05	06					01	02	03							01			01	02	03	04	05					01	02	03
03	04	05	06	07	08	09	07	08	09	10	11	12	13	04	05	06	07	08	09	10	02	03	04	05	06	07	08	06	07	08	09	10	11	12	04	05	06	07	08	09	10
10	11	12	13	14	15	16	14	15	16	17	18	19	20	11	12	13	14	15	16	17	09	10	11	12	13	14	15	13	14	15	16	17	18	19	11	12	13	14	15	16	17
17	18	19	20	21	22	23	21	22	23	24	25	26	27	18	19	20	21	22	23	24	16	17	18	19	20	21	22	20	21	22	23	24	25	26	18	19	20	21	22	23	24
24	25	26	27	28	29	30	28	29	30	31				25	26	27	28	29	30		23	24	25	26	27	28	29	27	28	29	30				25	26	27	28	29	30	31
31																					30	31																			

JUNE
WEEK 26

26 MONDAY
THINGS TO DO/NOTES

27 TUESDAY
THINGS TO DO/NOTES

28 WEDNESDAY
THINGS TO DO/NOTES

JANUARY	FEBRUARY	MARCH	APRIL	MAY	JUNE
M T W T F S S	M T W T F S S	M T W T F S S	M T W T F S S	M T W T F S S	M T W T F S S
01	01 02 03 04 05	01 02 03 04 05	01 02	01 02 03 04 05 06 07	01 02 03 04
02 03 04 05 06 07 08	06 07 08 09 10 11 12	06 07 08 09 10 11 12	03 04 05 06 07 08 09	08 09 10 11 12 13 14	05 06 07 08 09 10 11
09 10 11 12 13 14 15	13 14 15 16 17 18 19	13 14 15 16 17 18 19	10 11 12 13 14 15 16	15 16 17 18 19 20 21	12 13 14 15 16 17 18
16 17 18 19 20 21 22	20 21 22 23 24 25 26	20 21 22 23 24 25 26	17 18 19 20 21 22 23	22 23 24 25 26 27 28	19 20 21 22 23 24 25
23 24 25 26 27 28 29	27 28	27 28 29 30 31	24 25 26 27 28 29 30	29 30 31	26 27 28 29 30
30 31					

EID UL-ADHA

THURSDAY 29

THINGS TO DO/NOTES

FRIDAY 30

THINGS TO DO/NOTES

CANADA DAY (CAN)

SATURDAY 01

THINGS TO DO/NOTES

SUNDAY 02

THINGS TO DO/NOTES

	JULY		AUGUST		SEPTEMBER		OCTOBER		NOVEMBER		DECEMBER

JULY
M T W F S S
01 02
03 04 05 06 07 08 09
10 11 12 13 14 15 16
17 18 19 20 21 22 23
24 25 26 27 28 29 30
31

AUGUST
M T W F S S
01 02 03 04 05 06
07 08 09 10 11 12 13
14 15 16 17 18 19 20
21 22 23 24 25 26 27
28 29 30 31

SEPTEMBER
M T W F S S
01 02 03
04 05 06 07 08 09 10
11 12 13 14 15 16 17
18 19 20 21 22 23 24
25 26 27 28 29 30

OCTOBER
M T W F S S
01
02 03 04 05 06 07 08
09 10 11 12 13 14 15
16 17 18 19 20 21 22
23 24 25 26 27 28 29
30 31

NOVEMBER
M T W F S S
01 02 03 04 05
06 07 08 09 10 11 12
13 14 15 16 17 18 19
20 21 22 23 24 25 26
27 28 29 30

DECEMBER
M T W F S S
01 02 03
04 05 06 07 08 09 10
11 12 13 14 15 16 17
18 19 20 21 22 23 24
25 26 27 28 29 30 31

JULY
WEEK 27

03 MONDAY
THINGS TO DO/NOTES

04 TUESDAY
THINGS TO DO/NOTES

INDEPENDENCE DAY (USA)

05 WEDNESDAY
THINGS TO DO/NOTES

JANUARY	FEBRUARY	MARCH	APRIL	MAY	JUNE
M T W T F S S	M T W T F S S	M T W T F S S	M T W T F S S	M T W T F S S	M T W T F S S
01	01 02 03 04 05	01 02 03 04 05	01 02	01 02 03 04 05 06 07	01 02 03 04
02 03 04 05 06 07 08	06 07 08 09 10 11 12	06 07 08 09 10 11 12	03 04 05 06 07 08 09	08 09 10 11 12 13 14	05 06 07 08 09 10 11
09 10 11 12 13 14 15	13 14 15 16 17 18 19	13 14 15 16 17 18 19	10 11 12 13 14 15 16	15 16 17 18 19 20 21	12 13 14 15 16 17 18
16 17 18 19 20 21 22	20 21 22 23 24 25 26	20 21 22 23 24 25 26	17 18 19 20 21 22 23	22 23 24 25 26 27 28	19 20 21 22 23 24 25
23 24 25 26 27 28 29	27 28	27 28 29 30 31	24 25 26 27 28 29 30	29 30 31	26 27 28 29 30
30 31					

THURSDAY 06
THINGS TO DO/NOTES

FRIDAY 07
THINGS TO DO/NOTES

SATURDAY 08
THINGS TO DO/NOTES

SUNDAY 09
THINGS TO DO/NOTES

JULY							AUGUST							SEPTEMBER							OCTOBER							NOVEMBER							DECEMBER						
M	T	W	T	F	S	S	M	T	W	T	F	S	S	M	T	W	T	F	S	S	M	T	W	T	F	S	S	M	T	W	T	F	S	S	M	T	W	T	F	S	S
				01	02			01	02	03	04	05	06					01	02	03							01			01	02	03	04	05					01	02	03
03	04	05	06	07	08	09	07	08	09	10	11	12	13	04	05	06	07	08	09	10	02	03	04	05	06	07	08	06	07	08	09	10	11	12	04	05	06	07	08	09	10
10	11	12	13	14	15	16	14	15	16	17	18	19	20	11	12	13	14	15	16	17	09	10	11	12	13	14	15	13	14	15	16	17	18	19	11	12	13	14	15	16	17
17	18	19	20	21	22	23	21	22	23	24	25	26	27	18	19	20	21	22	23	24	16	17	18	19	20	21	22	20	21	22	23	24	25	26	18	19	20	21	22	23	24
24	25	26	27	28	29	30	28	29	30	31				25	26	27	28	29	30		23	24	25	26	27	28	29	27	28	29	30				25	26	27	28	29	30	31
31																					30	31																			

JULY
WEEK 28

10 MONDAY
THINGS TO DO/NOTES

11 TUESDAY
THINGS TO DO/NOTES

12 WEDNESDAY
THINGS TO DO/NOTES

BATTLE OF THE BOYNE (N. IRELAND)

JANUARY								FEBRUARY								MARCH								APRIL								MAY								JUNE						
M	T	W	T	F	S	S		M	T	W	T	F	S	S		M	T	W	T	F	S	S		M	T	W	T	F	S	S		M	T	W	T	F	S	S		M	T	W	T	F	S	S	
					01	02				01	02	03	04	05				01	02	03	04	05							01	02		01	02	03	04	05	06	07					01	02	03	04
02	03	04	05	06	07	08		06	07	08	09	10	11	12		06	07	08	09	10	11	12		03	04	05	06	07	08	09		08	09	10	11	12	13	14		05	06	07	08	09	10	11
09	10	11	12	13	14	15		13	14	15	16	17	18	19		13	14	15	16	17	18	19		10	11	12	13	14	15	16		15	16	17	18	19	20	21		12	13	14	15	16	17	18
16	17	18	19	20	21	22		20	21	22	23	24	25	26		20	21	22	23	24	25	26		17	18	19	20	21	22	23		22	23	24	25	26	27	28		19	20	21	22	23	24	25
23	24	25	26	27	28	29		27	28							27	28	29	30	31				24	25	26	27	28	29	30		29	30	31						26	27	28	29	30		
30	31																																											

JULY

THURSDAY 13

THINGS TO DO/NOTES

FRIDAY 14

THINGS TO DO/NOTES

SATURDAY 15

THINGS TO DO/NOTES

SUNDAY 16

THINGS TO DO/NOTES

JULY						
M	T	W	T	F	S	S
				01	02	
03	04	05	06	07	08	09
10	11	12	13	14	15	16
17	18	19	20	21	22	23
24	25	26	27	28	29	30
31						

AUGUST						
M	T	W	T	F	S	S
01	02	03	04	05	06	
07	08	09	10	11	12	13
14	15	16	17	18	19	20
21	22	23	24	25	26	27
28	29	30	31			

SEPTEMBER						
M	T	W	T	F	S	S
				01	02	03
04	05	06	07	08	09	10
11	12	13	14	15	16	17
18	19	20	21	22	23	24
25	26	27	28	29	30	

OCTOBER						
M	T	W	T	F	S	S
						01
02	03	04	05	06	07	08
09	10	11	12	13	14	15
16	17	18	19	20	21	22
23	24	25	26	27	28	29
30	31					

NOVEMBER						
M	T	W	T	F	S	S
	01	02	03	04	05	
06	07	08	09	10	11	12
13	14	15	16	17	18	19
20	21	22	23	24	25	26
27	28	29	30			

DECEMBER						
M	T	W	T	F	S	S
				01	02	03
04	05	06	07	08	09	10
11	12	13	14	15	16	17
18	19	20	21	22	23	24
25	26	27	28	29	30	31

JULY
WEEK 29

17 MONDAY
THINGS TO DO/NOTES

18 TUESDAY
THINGS TO DO/NOTES

19 WEDNESDAY
MUHARRAM/ISLAMIC NEW YEAR

THINGS TO DO/NOTES

JANUARY						
M	T	W	T	F	S	S
						01
02	03	04	05	06	07	08
09	10	11	12	13	14	15
16	17	18	19	20	21	22
23	24	25	26	27	28	29
30	31					

FEBRUARY						
M	T	W	T	F	S	S
		01	02	03	04	05
06	07	08	09	10	11	12
13	14	15	16	17	18	19
20	21	22	23	24	25	26
27	28					

MARCH						
M	T	W	T	F	S	S
		01	02	03	04	05
06	07	08	09	10	11	12
13	14	15	16	17	18	19
20	21	22	23	24	25	26
27	28	29	30	31		

APRIL						
M	T	W	T	F	S	S
					01	02
03	04	05	06	07	08	09
10	11	12	13	14	15	16
17	18	19	20	21	22	23
24	25	26	27	28	29	30

MAY						
M	T	W	T	F	S	S
01	02	03	04	05	06	07
08	09	10	11	12	13	14
15	16	17	18	19	20	21
22	23	24	25	26	27	28
29	30	31				

JUNE						
M	T	W	T	F	S	S
			01	02	03	04
05	06	07	08	09	10	11
12	13	14	15	16	17	18
19	20	21	22	23	24	25
26	27	28	29	30		

JULY
WEEK 29

THURSDAY 20
THINGS TO DO/NOTES

FRIDAY 21
THINGS TO DO/NOTES

SATURDAY 22
THINGS TO DO/NOTES

SUNDAY 23
THINGS TO DO/NOTES

JULY						
M	T	W	T	F	S	S
					01	02
03	04	05	06	07	08	09
10	11	12	13	14	15	16
17	18	19	20	21	22	23
24	25	26	27	28	29	30
31						

AUGUST						
M	T	W	T	F	S	S
	01	02	03	04	05	06
07	08	09	10	11	12	13
14	15	16	17	18	19	20
21	22	23	24	25	26	27
28	29	30	31			

SEPTEMBER						
M	T	W	T	F	S	S
				01	02	03
04	05	06	07	08	09	10
11	12	13	14	15	16	17
18	19	20	21	22	23	24
25	26	27	28	29	30	

OCTOBER						
M	T	W	T	F	S	S
						01
02	03	04	05	06	07	08
09	10	11	12	13	14	15
16	17	18	19	20	21	22
23	24	25	26	27	28	29
30	31					

NOVEMBER						
M	T	W	T	F	S	S
		01	02	03	04	05
06	07	08	09	10	11	12
13	14	15	16	17	18	19
20	21	22	23	24	25	26
27	28	29	30			

DECEMBER						
M	T	W	T	F	S	S
				01	02	03
04	05	06	07	08	09	10
11	12	13	14	15	16	17
18	19	20	21	22	23	24
25	26	27	28	29	30	31

JULY
WEEK 30

24 MONDAY
THINGS TO DO/NOTES

25 TUESDAY
THINGS TO DO/NOTES

26 WEDNESDAY
THINGS TO DO/NOTES

JANUARY	FEBRUARY	MARCH	APRIL	MAY	JUNE
M T W T F S S	M T W T F S S	M T W T F S S	M T W T F S S	M T W T F S S	M T W T F S S
01	01 02 03 04 05	01 02 03 04 05	01 02	01 02 03 04 05 06 07	01 02 03 04
02 03 04 05 06 07 08	06 07 08 09 10 11 12	06 07 08 09 10 11 12	03 04 05 06 07 08 09	08 09 10 11 12 13 14	05 06 07 08 09 10 11
09 10 11 12 13 14 15	13 14 15 16 17 18 19	13 14 15 16 17 18 19	10 11 12 13 14 15 16	15 16 17 18 19 20 21	12 13 14 15 16 17 18
16 17 18 19 20 21 22	20 21 22 23 24 25 26	20 21 22 23 24 25 26	17 18 19 20 21 22 23	22 23 24 25 26 27 28	19 20 21 22 23 24 25
23 24 25 26 27 28 29	27 28	27 28 29 30 31	24 25 26 27 28 29 30	29 30 31	26 27 28 29 30
30 31					

JULY
WEEK 30

TISHA B'AV

THURSDAY **27**

THINGS TO DO/NOTES

ASHURA

FRIDAY **28**

THINGS TO DO/NOTES

SATURDAY **29**

THINGS TO DO/NOTES

SUNDAY **30**

THINGS TO DO/NOTES

JULY								AUGUST								SEPTEMBER								OCTOBER								NOVEMBER								DECEMBER					
M	T	W	T	F	S	S		M	T	W	T	F	S	S		M	T	W	T	F	S	S		M	T	W	T	F	S	S		M	T	W	T	F	S	S		M	T	W	T	F	S	S
					01	02			01	02	03	04	05	06						01	02	03							01				01	02	03	04	05						01	02	03
03	04	05	06	07	08	09		07	08	09	10	11	12	13		04	05	06	07	08	09	10		02	03	04	05	06	07	08		06	07	08	09	10	11	12		04	05	06	07	08	09	10
10	11	12	13	14	15	16		14	15	16	17	18	19	20		11	12	13	14	15	16	17		09	10	11	12	13	14	15		13	14	15	16	17	18	19		11	12	13	14	15	16	17
17	18	19	20	21	22	23		21	22	23	24	25	26	27		18	19	20	21	22	23	24		16	17	18	19	20	21	22		20	21	22	23	24	25	26		18	19	20	21	22	23	24
24	25	26	27	28	29	30		28	29	30	31					25	26	27	28	29	30			23	24	25	26	27	28	29		27	28	29	30					25	26	27	28	29	30	31
31																							30	31																				

JULY
WEEK 31

AUGUST

31 MONDAY
THINGS TO DO/NOTES

01 TUESDAY
THINGS TO DO/NOTES

02 WEDNESDAY
THINGS TO DO/NOTES

JANUARY	FEBRUARY	MARCH	APRIL	MAY	JUNE
M T W T F S S	M T W T F S S	M T W T F S S	M T W T F S S	M T W T F S S	M T W T F S S
01	01 02 03 04 05	01 02 03 04 05	01 02	01 02 03 04 05 06 07	01 02 03 04
02 03 04 05 06 07 08	06 07 08 09 10 11 12	06 07 08 09 10 11 12	03 04 05 06 07 08 09	08 09 10 11 12 13 14	05 06 07 08 09 10 11
09 10 11 12 13 14 15	13 14 15 16 17 18 19	13 14 15 16 17 18 19	10 11 12 13 14 15 16	15 16 17 18 19 20 21	12 13 14 15 16 17 18
16 17 18 19 20 21 22	20 21 22 23 24 25 26	20 21 22 23 24 25 26	17 18 19 20 21 22 23	22 23 24 25 26 27 28	19 20 21 22 23 24 25
23 24 25 26 27 28 29	27 28	27 28 29 30 31	24 25 26 27 28 29 30	29 30 31	26 27 28 29 30
30 31					

THURSDAY 03
THINGS TO DO/NOTES

FRIDAY 04
THINGS TO DO/NOTES

SATURDAY 05
THINGS TO DO/NOTES

SUNDAY 06
THINGS TO DO/NOTES

JULY						
M	T	W	T	F	S	S
					01	02
03	04	05	06	07	08	09
10	11	12	13	14	15	16
17	18	19	20	21	22	23
24	25	26	27	28	29	30
31						

AUGUST						
M	T	W	T	F	S	S
	01	02	03	04	05	06
07	08	09	10	11	12	13
14	15	16	17	18	19	20
21	22	23	24	25	26	27
28	29	30	31			

SEPTEMBER						
M	T	W	T	F	S	S
				01	02	03
04	05	06	07	08	09	10
11	12	13	14	15	16	17
18	19	20	21	22	23	24
25	26	27	28	29	30	

OCTOBER						
M	T	W	T	F	S	S
						01
02	03	04	05	06	07	08
09	10	11	12	13	14	15
16	17	18	19	20	21	22
23	24	25	26	27	28	29
30	31					

NOVEMBER						
M	T	W	T	F	S	S
		01	02	03	04	05
06	07	08	09	10	11	12
13	14	15	16	17	18	19
20	21	22	23	24	25	26
27	28	29	30			

DECEMBER						
M	T	W	T	F	S	S
				01	02	03
04	05	06	07	08	09	10
11	12	13	14	15	16	17
18	19	20	21	22	23	24
25	26	27	28	29	30	31

AUGUST
WEEK 32

07 MONDAY
SUMMER BANK HOLIDAY (SCOTLAND & ROI)

THINGS TO DO/NOTES

08 TUESDAY
THINGS TO DO/NOTES

09 WEDNESDAY
THINGS TO DO/NOTES

JANUARY								FEBRUARY								MARCH								APRIL								MAY								JUNE						
M	T	W	T	F	S	S		M	T	W	T	F	S	S		M	T	W	T	F	S	S		M	T	W	T	F	S	S		M	T	W	T	F	S	S		M	T	W	T	F	S	S
						01				01	02	03	04	05				01	02	03	04	05						01	02		01	02	03	04	05	06	07					01	02	03	04
02	03	04	05	06	07	08		06	07	08	09	10	11	12		06	07	08	09	10	11	12		03	04	05	06	07	08	09		08	09	10	11	12	13	14		05	06	07	08	09	10	11
09	10	11	12	13	14	15		13	14	15	16	17	18	19		13	14	15	16	17	18	19		10	11	12	13	14	15	16		15	16	17	18	19	20	21		12	13	14	15	16	17	18
16	17	18	19	20	21	22		20	21	22	23	24	25	26		20	21	22	23	24	25	26		17	18	19	20	21	22	23		22	23	24	25	26	27	28		19	20	21	22	23	24	25
23	24	25	26	27	28	29		27	28							27	28	29	30	31				24	25	26	27	28	29	30		29	30	31						26	27	28	29	30		
30	31																																												

AUGUST
WEEK 32

THURSDAY 10
THINGS TO DO/NOTES

FRIDAY 11
THINGS TO DO/NOTES

SATURDAY 12
THINGS TO DO/NOTES

SUNDAY 13
THINGS TO DO/NOTES

JULY								AUGUST								SEPTEMBER								OCTOBER								NOVEMBER								DECEMBER						
M	T	W	T	F	S	S		M	T	W	T	F	S	S		M	T	W	T	F	S	S		M	T	W	T	F	S	S		M	T	W	T	F	S	S		M	T	W	T	F	S	S
					01	02			01	02	03	04	05	06						01	02	03							01			01	02	03	04	05							01	02	03
03	04	05	06	07	08	09		07	08	09	10	11	12	13		04	05	06	07	08	09	10		02	03	04	05	06	07	08		06	07	08	09	10	11	12		04	05	06	07	08	09	10
10	11	12	13	14	15	16		14	15	16	17	18	19	20		11	12	13	14	15	16	17		09	10	11	12	13	14	15		13	14	15	16	17	18	19		11	12	13	14	15	16	17
17	18	19	20	21	22	23		21	22	23	24	25	26	27		18	19	20	21	22	23	24		16	17	18	19	20	21	22		20	21	22	23	24	25	26		18	19	20	21	22	23	24
24	25	26	27	28	29	30		28	29	30	31					25	26	27	28	29	30			23	24	25	26	27	28	29		27	28	29	30					25	26	27	28	29	30	31
31																							30	31																				

AUGUST
WEEK 33

14 MONDAY
THINGS TO DO/NOTES

15 TUESDAY
THINGS TO DO/NOTES

ASSUMPTION OF MARY

16 WEDNESDAY
THINGS TO DO/NOTES

JANUARY	FEBRUARY	MARCH	APRIL	MAY	JUNE
M T W T F S S	M T W T F S S	M T W T F S S	M T W T F S S	M T W T F S S	M T W T F S S
01	01 02 03 04 05	01 02 03 04 05	01 02	01 02 03 04 05 06 07	01 02 03 04
02 03 04 05 06 07 08	06 07 08 09 10 11 12	06 07 08 09 10 11 12	03 04 05 06 07 08 09	08 09 10 11 12 13 14	05 06 07 08 09 10 11
09 10 11 12 13 14 15	13 14 15 16 17 18 19	13 14 15 16 17 18 19	10 11 12 13 14 15 16	15 16 17 18 19 20 21	12 13 14 15 16 17 18
16 17 18 19 20 21 22	20 21 22 23 24 25 26	20 21 22 23 24 25 26	17 18 19 20 21 22 23	22 23 24 25 26 27 28	19 20 21 22 23 24 25
23 24 25 26 27 28 29	27 28	27 28 29 30 31	24 25 26 27 28 29 30	29 30 31	26 27 28 29 30
30 31					

THURSDAY · 17
THINGS TO DO/NOTES

FRIDAY · 18
THINGS TO DO/NOTES

SATURDAY · 19
THINGS TO DO/NOTES

SUNDAY · 20
THINGS TO DO/NOTES

JULY							AUGUST							SEPTEMBER							OCTOBER							NOVEMBER							DECEMBER						
M	T	W	T	F	S	S	M	T	W	T	F	S	S	M	T	W	T	F	S	S	M	T	W	T	F	S	S	M	T	W	T	F	S	S	M	T	W	T	F	S	S
					01	02		01	02	03	04	05	06					01	02	03						01			01	02	03	04	05					01	02	03
03	04	05	06	07	08	09	07	08	09	10	11	12	13	04	05	06	07	08	09	10	02	03	04	05	06	07	08	06	07	08	09	10	11	12	04	05	06	07	08	09	10
10	11	12	13	14	15	16	14	15	16	17	18	19	20	11	12	13	14	15	16	17	09	10	11	12	13	14	15	13	14	15	16	17	18	19	11	12	13	14	15	16	17
17	18	19	20	21	22	23	21	22	23	24	25	26	27	18	19	20	21	22	23	24	16	17	18	19	20	21	22	20	21	22	23	24	25	26	18	19	20	21	22	23	24
24	25	26	27	28	29	30	28	29	30	31				25	26	27	28	29	30		23	24	25	26	27	28	29	27	28	29	30				25	26	27	28	29	30	31
31																					30	31																			

AUGUST
WEEK 34

21 MONDAY
THINGS TO DO/NOTES

22 TUESDAY
THINGS TO DO/NOTES

23 WEDNESDAY
THINGS TO DO/NOTES

JANUARY	FEBRUARY	MARCH	APRIL	MAY	JUNE
M T W T F S S	M T W T F S S	M T W T F S S	M T W T F S S	M T W T F S S	M T W T F S S
01	01 02 03 04 05	01 02 03 04 05	01 02	01 02 03 04 05 06 07	01 02 03 04
02 03 04 05 06 07 08	06 07 08 09 10 11 12	06 07 08 09 10 11 12	03 04 05 06 07 08 09	08 09 10 11 12 13 14	05 06 07 08 09 10 11
09 10 11 12 13 14 15	13 14 15 16 17 18 19	13 14 15 16 17 18 19	10 11 12 13 14 15 16	15 16 17 18 19 20 21	12 13 14 15 16 17 18
16 17 18 19 20 21 22	20 21 22 23 24 25 26	20 21 22 23 24 25 26	17 18 19 20 21 22 23	22 23 24 25 26 27 28	19 20 21 22 23 24 25
23 24 25 26 27 28 29	27 28	27 28 29 30 31	24 25 26 27 28 29 30	29 30 31	26 27 28 29 30
30 31					

AUGUST
WEEK 34

THURSDAY 24
THINGS TO DO/NOTES

FRIDAY 25
THINGS TO DO/NOTES

SATURDAY 26
THINGS TO DO/NOTES

SUNDAY 27
THINGS TO DO/NOTES

JULY							AUGUST							SEPTEMBER							OCTOBER							NOVEMBER							DECEMBER						
M	T	W	T	F	S	S	M	T	W	T	F	S	S	M	T	W	T	F	S	S	M	T	W	T	F	S	S	M	T	W	T	F	S	S	M	T	W	T	F	S	S
					01	02		01	02	03	04	05	06					01	02	03						01			01	02	03	04	05					01	02	03
03	04	05	06	07	08	09	07	08	09	10	11	12	13	04	05	06	07	08	09	10	02	03	04	05	06	07	08	06	07	08	09	10	11	12	04	05	06	07	08	09	10
10	11	12	13	14	15	16	14	15	16	17	18	19	20	11	12	13	14	15	16	17	09	10	11	12	13	14	15	13	14	15	16	17	18	19	11	12	13	14	15	16	17
17	18	19	20	21	22	23	21	22	23	24	25	26	27	18	19	20	21	22	23	24	16	17	18	19	20	21	22	20	21	22	23	24	25	26	18	19	20	21	22	23	24
24	25	26	27	28	29	30	28	29	30	31				25	26	27	28	29	30		23	24	25	26	27	28	29	27	28	29	30				25	26	27	28	29	30	31
31																					30	31																			

AUGUST

28 MONDAY
THINGS TO DO/NOTES

SUMMER BANK HOLIDAY (UK EXCEPT SCOTLAND)

29 TUESDAY
THINGS TO DO/NOTES

30 WEDNESDAY
THINGS TO DO/NOTES

RAKSHA BANDHAN

JANUARY							FEBRUARY							MARCH							APRIL							MAY							JUNE						
M	T	W	T	F	S	S	M	T	W	T	F	S	S	M	T	W	T	F	S	S	M	T	W	T	F	S	S	M	T	W	T	F	S	S	M	T	W	T	F	S	S
						01			01	02	03	04	05			01	02	03	04	05						01	02	01	02	03	04	05	06	07				01	02	03	04
02	03	04	05	06	07	08	06	07	08	09	10	11	12	06	07	08	09	10	11	12	03	04	05	06	07	08	09	08	09	10	11	12	13	14	05	06	07	08	09	10	11
09	10	11	12	13	14	15	13	14	15	16	17	18	19	13	14	15	16	17	18	19	10	11	12	13	14	15	16	15	16	17	18	19	20	21	12	13	14	15	16	17	18
16	17	18	19	20	21	22	20	21	22	23	24	25	26	20	21	22	23	24	25	26	17	18	19	20	21	22	23	22	23	24	25	26	27	28	19	20	21	22	23	24	25
23	24	25	26	27	28	29	27	28						27	28	29	30	31			24	25	26	27	28	29	30	29	30	31					26	27	28	29	30		
30	31																																								

THURSDAY **31**

THINGS TO DO/NOTES

FRIDAY **01**

THINGS TO DO/NOTES

SATURDAY **02**

THINGS TO DO/NOTES

SUNDAY **03**

THINGS TO DO/NOTES

JULY								AUGUST								SEPTEMBER								OCTOBER								NOVEMBER								DECEMBER						
M	T	W	T	F	S	S		M	T	W	T	F	S	S		M	T	W	T	F	S	S		M	T	W	T	F	S	S		M	T	W	T	F	S	S		M	T	W	T	F	S	S
				01	02								01	02					01	02	03							01							01							01	02	03
03	04	05	06	07	08	09		01	02	03	04	05	06		04	05	06	07	08	09	10		02	03	04	05	06	07	08		06	07	08	09	10	11	12		04	05	06	07	08	09	10
10	11	12	13	14	15	16		07	08	09	10	11	12	13		11	12	13	14	15	16	17		09	10	11	12	13	14	15		13	14	15	16	17	18	19		11	12	13	14	15	16	17
17	18	19	20	21	22	23		14	15	16	17	18	19	20		18	19	20	21	22	23	24		16	17	18	19	20	21	22		20	21	22	23	24	25	26		18	19	20	21	22	23	24
24	25	26	27	28	29	30		21	22	23	24	25	26	27		25	26	27	28	29	30			23	24	25	26	27	28	29		27	28	29	30					25	26	27	28	29	30	31
31								28	29	30	31													30	31																			

SEPTEMBER
WEEK 36

04 MONDAY
LABOR DAY (USA, CAN)

THINGS TO DO/NOTES

05 TUESDAY
THINGS TO DO/NOTES

06 WEDNESDAY
JANMASHTAMI

THINGS TO DO/NOTES

JANUARY	FEBRUARY	MARCH	APRIL	MAY	JUNE
M T W T F S S	M T W T F S S	M T W T F S S	M T W T F S S	M T W T F S S	M T W T F S S
01	01 02 03 04 05	01 02 03 04 05	01 02	01 02 03 04 05 06 07	01 02 03 04
02 03 04 05 06 07 08	06 07 08 09 10 11 12	06 07 08 09 10 11 12	03 04 05 06 07 08 09	08 09 10 11 12 13 14	05 06 07 08 09 10 11
09 10 11 12 13 14 15	13 14 15 16 17 18 19	13 14 15 16 17 18 19	10 11 12 13 14 15 16	15 16 17 18 19 20 21	12 13 14 15 16 17 18
16 17 18 19 20 21 22	20 21 22 23 24 25 26	20 21 22 23 24 25 26	17 18 19 20 21 22 23	22 23 24 25 26 27 28	19 20 21 22 23 24 25
23 24 25 26 27 28 29	27 28	27 28 29 30 31	24 25 26 27 28 29 30	29 30 31	26 27 28 29 30
30 31					

SEPTEMBER
WEEK 36

THURSDAY 07
THINGS TO DO/NOTES

FRIDAY 08
THINGS TO DO/NOTES

SATURDAY 09
THINGS TO DO/NOTES

SUNDAY 10
THINGS TO DO/NOTES

JULY						
M	T	W	T	F	S	S
				01	02
03	04	05	06	07	08	09
10	11	12	13	14	15	16
17	18	19	20	21	22	23
24	25	26	27	28	29	30
31						

AUGUST						
M	T	W	T	F	S	S
	01	02	03	04	05	06
07	08	09	10	11	12	13
14	15	16	17	18	19	20
21	22	23	24	25	26	27
28	29	30	31			

SEPTEMBER						
M	T	W	T	F	S	S
				01	02	03
04	05	06	07	08	09	10
11	12	13	14	15	16	17
18	19	20	21	22	23	24
25	26	27	28	29	30	

OCTOBER						
M	T	W	T	F	S	S
						01
02	03	04	05	06	07	08
09	10	11	12	13	14	15
16	17	18	19	20	21	22
23	24	25	26	27	28	29
30	31					

NOVEMBER						
M	T	W	T	F	S	S
		01	02	03	04	05
06	07	08	09	10	11	12
13	14	15	16	17	18	19
20	21	22	23	24	25	26
27	28	29	30			

DECEMBER						
M	T	W	T	F	S	S
				01	02	03
04	05	06	07	08	09	10
11	12	13	14	15	16	17
18	19	20	21	22	23	24
25	26	27	28	29	30	31

SEPTEMBER
WEEK 37

11 MONDAY
THINGS TO DO/NOTES

12 TUESDAY
THINGS TO DO/NOTES

13 WEDNESDAY
THINGS TO DO/NOTES

JANUARY								FEBRUARY								MARCH								APRIL								MAY								JUNE						
M	T	W	T	F	S	S		M	T	W	T	F	S	S		M	T	W	T	F	S	S		M	T	W	T	F	S	S		M	T	W	T	F	S	S		M	T	W	T	F	S	S
						01					01	02	03	04	05					01	02	03	04	05						01	02		01	02	03	04	05	06	07					01	02	03	04
02	03	04	05	06	07	08		06	07	08	09	10	11	12		06	07	08	09	10	11	12		03	04	05	06	07	08	09		08	09	10	11	12	13	14		05	06	07	08	09	10	11
09	10	11	12	13	14	15		13	14	15	16	17	18	19		13	14	15	16	17	18	19		10	11	12	13	14	15	16		15	16	17	18	19	20	21		12	13	14	15	16	17	18
16	17	18	19	20	21	22		20	21	22	23	24	25	26		20	21	22	23	24	25	26		17	18	19	20	21	22	23		22	23	24	25	26	27	28		19	20	21	22	23	24	25
23	24	25	26	27	28	29		27	28							27	28	29	30	31				24	25	26	27	28	29	30		29	30	31						26	27	28	29	30		
30	31																																												

THURSDAY 14
THINGS TO DO/NOTES

FRIDAY 15
THINGS TO DO/NOTES

ROSH HASHANA

SATURDAY 16
THINGS TO DO/NOTES

SUNDAY 17
THINGS TO DO/NOTES

JULY						
M	T	W	T	F	S	S
					01	02
03	04	05	06	07	08	09
10	11	12	13	14	15	16
17	18	19	20	21	22	23
24	25	26	27	28	29	30
31						

AUGUST						
M	T	W	T	F	S	S
	01	02	03	04	05	06
07	08	09	10	11	12	13
14	15	16	17	18	19	20
21	22	23	24	25	26	27
28	29	30	31			

SEPTEMBER						
M	T	W	T	F	S	S
				01	02	03
04	05	06	07	08	09	10
11	12	13	14	15	16	17
18	19	20	21	22	23	24
25	26	27	28	29	30	

OCTOBER						
M	T	W	T	F	S	S
						01
02	03	04	05	06	07	08
09	10	11	12	13	14	15
16	17	18	19	20	21	22
23	24	25	26	27	28	29
30	31					

NOVEMBER						
M	T	W	T	F	S	S
		01	02	03	04	05
06	07	08	09	10	11	12
13	14	15	16	17	18	19
20	21	22	23	24	25	26
27	28	29	30			

DECEMBER						
M	T	W	T	F	S	S
				01	02	03
04	05	06	07	08	09	10
11	12	13	14	15	16	17
18	19	20	21	22	23	24
25	26	27	28	29	30	31

SEPTEMBER
WEEK 38

18 MONDAY
THINGS TO DO/NOTES

19 TUESDAY
THINGS TO DO/NOTES

GANESH CHATURTHI

20 WEDNESDAY
THINGS TO DO/NOTES

JANUARY							
M	T	W	T	F	S	S	
					01	
02	03	04	05	06	07	08
09	10	11	12	13	14	15
16	17	18	19	20	21	22
23	24	25	26	27	28	29
30	31					

FEBRUARY						
M	T	W	T	F	S	S
		01	02	03	04	05
06	07	08	09	10	11	12
13	14	15	16	17	18	19
20	21	22	23	24	25	26
27	28					

MARCH						
M	T	W	T	F	S	S
		01	02	03	04	05
06	07	08	09	10	11	12
13	14	15	16	17	18	19
20	21	22	23	24	25	26
27	28	29	30	31		

APRIL						
M	T	W	T	F	S	S
					01	02
03	04	05	06	07	08	09
10	11	12	13	14	15	16
17	18	19	20	21	22	23
24	25	26	27	28	29	30

MAY						
M	T	W	T	F	S	S
01	02	03	04	05	06	07
08	09	10	11	12	13	14
15	16	17	18	19	20	21
22	23	24	25	26	27	28
29	30	31				

JUNE						
M	T	W	T	F	S	S
		01	02	03	04
05	06	07	08	09	10	11
12	13	14	15	16	17	18
19	20	21	22	23	24	25
26	27	28	29	30		

SEPTEMBER
WEEK 38

THURSDAY 21
THINGS TO DO/NOTES

FRIDAY 22
THINGS TO DO/NOTES

AUTUMN EQUINOX

SATURDAY 23
THINGS TO DO/NOTES

SUNDAY 24
THINGS TO DO/NOTES

JULY						
M	T	W	T	F	S	S
					01	02
03	04	05	06	07	08	09
10	11	12	13	14	15	16
17	18	19	20	21	22	23
24	25	26	27	28	29	30
31						

AUGUST						
M	T	W	T	F	S	S
01	02	03	04	05	06	
07	08	09	10	11	12	13
14	15	16	17	18	19	20
21	22	23	24	25	26	27
28	29	30	31			

SEPTEMBER						
M	T	W	T	F	S	S
				01	02	03
04	05	06	07	08	09	10
11	12	13	14	15	16	17
18	19	20	21	22	23	24
25	26	27	28	29	30	

OCTOBER						
M	T	W	T	F	S	S
						01
02	03	04	05	06	07	08
09	10	11	12	13	14	15
16	17	18	19	20	21	22
23	24	25	26	27	28	29
30	31					

NOVEMBER						
M	T	W	T	F	S	S
		01	02	03	04	05
06	07	08	09	10	11	12
13	14	15	16	17	18	19
20	21	22	23	24	25	26
27	28	29	30			

DECEMBER						
M	T	W	T	F	S	S
				01	02	03
04	05	06	07	08	09	10
11	12	13	14	15	16	17
18	19	20	21	22	23	24
25	26	27	28	29	30	31

SEPTEMBER

25 MONDAY
THINGS TO DO/NOTES

YOM KIPPUR

26 TUESDAY
THINGS TO DO/NOTES

27 WEDNESDAY
THINGS TO DO/NOTES

MILAD UN NABI (MAWLID)/THE PROPHET'S BIRTHDAY

JANUARY								FEBRUARY								MARCH								APRIL								MAY								JUNE						
M	T	W	T	F	S	S		M	T	W	T	F	S	S		M	T	W	T	F	S	S		M	T	W	T	F	S	S		M	T	W	T	F	S	S		M	T	W	T	F	S	S
						01				01	02	03	04	05				01	02	03	04	05							01	02		01	02	03	04	05	06	07						01	02	03	04
02	03	04	05	06	07	08		06	07	08	09	10	11	12		06	07	08	09	10	11	12		03	04	05	06	07	08	09		08	09	10	11	12	13	14		05	06	07	08	09	10	11
09	10	11	12	13	14	15		13	14	15	16	17	18	19		13	14	15	16	17	18	19		10	11	12	13	14	15	16		15	16	17	18	19	20	21		12	13	14	15	16	17	18
16	17	18	19	20	21	22		20	21	22	23	24	25	26		20	21	22	23	24	25	26		17	18	19	20	21	22	23		22	23	24	25	26	27	28		19	20	21	22	23	24	25
23	24	25	26	27	28	29		27	28							27	28	29	30	31				24	25	26	27	28	29	30		29	30	31						26	27	28	29	30		
30	31																																										

SEPTEMBER OCTOBER

THURSDAY 28

THINGS TO DO/NOTES

FRIDAY 29

THINGS TO DO/NOTES

FIRST DAY OF SUKKOT

SATURDAY 30

THINGS TO DO/NOTES

SUNDAY 01

THINGS TO DO/NOTES

JULY	AUGUST	SEPTEMBER	OCTOBER	NOVEMBER	DECEMBER
M T W T F S S	M T W T F S S	M T W T F S S	M T W T F S S	M T W T F S S	M T W T F S S
01 02	01 02 03 04 05 06	01 02 03	01	01 02 03 04 05	01 02 03
03 04 05 06 07 08 09	07 08 09 10 11 12 13	04 05 06 07 08 09 10	02 03 04 05 06 07 08	06 07 08 09 10 11 12	04 05 06 07 08 09 10
10 11 12 13 14 15 16	14 15 16 17 18 19 20	11 12 13 14 15 16 17	09 10 11 12 13 14 15	13 14 15 16 17 18 19	11 12 13 14 15 16 17
17 18 19 20 21 22 23	21 22 23 24 25 26 27	18 19 20 21 22 23 24	16 17 18 19 20 21 22	20 21 22 23 24 25 26	18 19 20 21 22 23 24
24 25 26 27 28 29 30	28 29 30 31	25 26 27 28 29 30	23 24 25 26 27 28 29	27 28 29 30	25 26 27 28 29 30 31
31			30 31		

02 MONDAY

THINGS TO DO/NOTES

03 TUESDAY

THINGS TO DO/NOTES

04 WEDNESDAY

THINGS TO DO/NOTES

FEAST OF ST FRANCIS OF ASSISI

JANUARY	FEBRUARY	MARCH	APRIL	MAY	JUNE
M T W T F S S	M T W T F S S	M T W T F S S	M T W T F S S	M T W T F S S	M T W T F S S
01	01 02 03 04 05	01 02 03 04 05	01 02	01 02 03 04 05 06 07	01 02 03 04
02 03 04 05 06 07 08	06 07 08 09 10 11 12	06 07 08 09 10 11 12	03 04 05 06 07 08 09	08 09 10 11 12 13 14	05 06 07 08 09 10 11
09 10 11 12 13 14 15	13 14 15 16 17 18 19	13 14 15 16 17 18 19	10 11 12 13 14 15 16	15 16 17 18 19 20 21	12 13 14 15 16 17 18
16 17 18 19 20 21 22	20 21 22 23 24 25 26	20 21 22 23 24 25 26	17 18 19 20 21 22 23	22 23 24 25 26 27 28	19 20 21 22 23 24 25
23 24 25 26 27 28 29	27 28	27 28 29 30 31	24 25 26 27 28 29 30	29 30 31	26 27 28 29 30
30 31					

OCTOBER
WEEK 40

THURSDAY 05
THINGS TO DO/NOTES

HOSHANA RABBAH

FRIDAY 06
THINGS TO DO/NOTES

SATURDAY 07
THINGS TO DO/NOTES

SUNDAY 08
THINGS TO DO/NOTES

JULY								AUGUST								SEPTEMBER								OCTOBER								NOVEMBER								DECEMBER						
M	T	W	T	F	S	S		M	T	W	T	F	S	S		M	T	W	T	F	S	S		M	T	W	T	F	S	S		M	T	W	T	F	S	S		M	T	W	T	F	S	S
					01	02					01	02	03	04	05	06						01	02	03							01			01	02	03	04	05						01	02	03
03	04	05	06	07	08	09		07	08	09	10	11	12	13		04	05	06	07	08	09	10		02	03	04	05	06	07	08		06	07	08	09	10	11	12		04	05	06	07	08	09	10
10	11	12	13	14	15	16		14	15	16	17	18	19	20		11	12	13	14	15	16	17		09	10	11	12	13	14	15		13	14	15	16	17	18	19		11	12	13	14	15	16	17
17	18	19	20	21	22	23		21	22	23	24	25	26	27		18	19	20	21	22	23	24		16	17	18	19	20	21	22		20	21	22	23	24	25	26		18	19	20	21	22	23	24
24	25	26	27	28	29	30		28	29	30	31					25	26	27	28	29	30			23	24	25	26	27	28	29		27	28	29	30					25	26	27	28	29	30	31
31																							30	31																				

OCTOBER
WEEK 41

09 MONDAY
THINGS TO DO/NOTES

THANKSGIVING DAY (CAN); COLUMBUS DAY (USA)

10 TUESDAY
THINGS TO DO/NOTES

11 WEDNESDAY
THINGS TO DO/NOTES

JANUARY	FEBRUARY	MARCH	APRIL	MAY	JUNE
M T W T F S S	M T W T F S S	M T W T F S S	M T W T F S S	M T W T F S S	M T W T F S S
01	01 02 03 04 05	01 02 03 04 05	01 02	01 02 03 04 05 06 07	01 02 03 04
02 03 04 05 06 07 08	06 07 08 09 10 11 12	06 07 08 09 10 11 12	03 04 05 06 07 08 09	08 09 10 11 12 13 14	05 06 07 08 09 10 11
09 10 11 12 13 14 15	13 14 15 16 17 18 19	13 14 15 16 17 18 19	10 11 12 13 14 15 16	15 16 17 18 19 20 21	12 13 14 15 16 17 18
16 17 18 19 20 21 22	20 21 22 23 24 25 26	20 21 22 23 24 25 26	17 18 19 20 21 22 23	22 23 24 25 26 27 28	19 20 21 22 23 24 25
23 24 25 26 27 28 29	27 28	27 28 29 30 31	24 25 26 27 28 29 30	29 30 31	26 27 28 29 30
30 31					

OCTOBER
WEEK 41

THURSDAY 12
THINGS TO DO/NOTES

FRIDAY 13
THINGS TO DO/NOTES

SATURDAY 14
THINGS TO DO/NOTES

NAVRATRI

SUNDAY 15
THINGS TO DO/NOTES

JULY							AUGUST							SEPTEMBER							OCTOBER							NOVEMBER							DECEMBER						
M	T	W	T	F	S	S	M	T	W	T	F	S	S	M	T	W	T	F	S	S	M	T	W	T	F	S	S	M	T	W	T	F	S	S	M	T	W	T	F	S	S
					01	02		01	02	03	04	05	06					01	02	03							01			01	02	03	04	05					01	02	03
03	04	05	06	07	08	09	07	08	09	10	11	12	13	04	05	06	07	08	09	10	02	03	04	05	06	07	08	06	07	08	09	10	11	12	04	05	06	07	08	09	10
10	11	12	13	14	15	16	14	15	16	17	18	19	20	11	12	13	14	15	16	17	09	10	11	12	13	14	15	13	14	15	16	17	18	19	11	12	13	14	15	16	17
17	18	19	20	21	22	23	21	22	23	24	25	26	27	18	19	20	21	22	23	24	16	17	18	19	20	21	22	20	21	22	23	24	25	26	18	19	20	21	22	23	24
24	25	26	27	28	29	30	28	29	30	31				25	26	27	28	29	30		23	24	25	26	27	28	29	27	28	29	30				25	26	27	28	29	30	31
31																					30	31																			

OCTOBER
WEEK 42

16 MONDAY
THINGS TO DO/NOTES

17 TUESDAY
THINGS TO DO/NOTES

18 WEDNESDAY
THINGS TO DO/NOTES

JANUARY	FEBRUARY	MARCH	APRIL	MAY	JUNE
M T W T F S S	M T W T F S S	M T W T F S S	M T W T F S S	M T W T F S S	M T W T F S S
01	01 02 03 04 05	01 02 03 04 05	01 02	01 02 03 04 05 06 07	01 02 03 04
02 03 04 05 06 07 08	06 07 08 09 10 11 12	06 07 08 09 10 11 12	03 04 05 06 07 08 09	08 09 10 11 12 13 14	05 06 07 08 09 10 11
09 10 11 12 13 14 15	13 14 15 16 17 18 19	13 14 15 16 17 18 19	10 11 12 13 14 15 16	15 16 17 18 19 20 21	12 13 14 15 16 17 18
16 17 18 19 20 21 22	20 21 22 23 24 25 26	20 21 22 23 24 25 26	17 18 19 20 21 22 23	22 23 24 25 26 27 28	19 20 21 22 23 24 25
23 24 25 26 27 28 29	27 28	27 28 29 30 31	24 25 26 27 28 29 30	29 30 31	26 27 28 29 30
30 31					

OCTOBER
WEEK 42

THURSDAY 19
THINGS TO DO/NOTES

FRIDAY 20
THINGS TO DO/NOTES

SATURDAY 21
THINGS TO DO/NOTES

SUNDAY 22
THINGS TO DO/NOTES

OCTOBER
WEEK 43

23 MONDAY
THINGS TO DO/NOTES

DUSSEHRA; LABOUR DAY (NZ)

24 TUESDAY
THINGS TO DO/NOTES

25 WEDNESDAY
THINGS TO DO/NOTES

JANUARY						
M	T	W	T	F	S	S
						01
02	03	04	05	06	07	08
09	10	11	12	13	14	15
16	17	18	19	20	21	22
23	24	25	26	27	28	29
30	31					

FEBRUARY						
M	T	W	T	F	S	S
		01	02	03	04	05
06	07	08	09	10	11	12
13	14	15	16	17	18	19
20	21	22	23	24	25	26
27	28					

MARCH						
M	T	W	T	F	S	S
		01	02	03	04	05
06	07	08	09	10	11	12
13	14	15	16	17	18	19
20	21	22	23	24	25	26
27	28	29	30	31		

APRIL						
M	T	W	T	F	S	S
					01	02
03	04	05	06	07	08	09
10	11	12	13	14	15	16
17	18	19	20	21	22	23
24	25	26	27	28	29	30

MAY						
M	T	W	T	F	S	S
01	02	03	04	05	06	07
08	09	10	11	12	13	14
15	16	17	18	19	20	21
22	23	24	25	26	27	28
29	30	31				

JUNE						
M	T	W	T	F	S	S
			01	02	03	04
05	06	07	08	09	10	11
12	13	14	15	16	17	18
19	20	21	22	23	24	25
26	27	28	29	30		

OCTOBER
WEEK 43

THURSDAY 26
THINGS TO DO/NOTES

FRIDAY 27
THINGS TO DO/NOTES

SATURDAY 28
THINGS TO DO/NOTES

BRITISH SUMMER TIME ENDS

SUNDAY 29
THINGS TO DO/NOTES

JULY	AUGUST	SEPTEMBER	OCTOBER	NOVEMBER	DECEMBER
M T W T F S S	M T W T F S S	M T W T F S S	M T W T F S S	M T W T F S S	M T W T F S S
01 02	01 02 03 04 05 06	01 02 03	01	01 02 03 04 05	01 02 03
03 04 05 06 07 08 09	07 08 09 10 11 12 13	04 05 06 07 08 09 10	02 03 04 05 06 07 08	06 07 08 09 10 11 12	04 05 06 07 08 09 10
10 11 12 13 14 15 16	14 15 16 17 18 19 20	11 12 13 14 15 16 17	09 10 11 12 13 14 15	13 14 15 16 17 18 19	11 12 13 14 15 16 17
17 18 19 20 21 22 23	21 22 23 24 25 26 27	18 19 20 21 22 23 24	16 17 18 19 20 21 22	20 21 22 23 24 25 26	18 19 20 21 22 23 24
24 25 26 27 28 29 30	28 29 30 31	25 26 27 28 29 30	23 24 25 26 27 28 29	27 28 29 30	25 26 27 28 29 30 31
31			30 31		

OCTOBER
WEEK 44

NOVEMBER

30 MONDAY
OCTOBER BANK HOLIDAY (ROI)

THINGS TO DO/NOTES

31 TUESDAY
HALLOWEEN

THINGS TO DO/NOTES

01 WEDNESDAY
ALL SAINTS' DAY

THINGS TO DO/NOTES

JANUARY							FEBRUARY							MARCH							APRIL							MAY							JUNE						
M	T	W	T	F	S	S	M	T	W	T	F	S	S	M	T	W	T	F	S	S	M	T	W	T	F	S	S	M	T	W	T	F	S	S	M	T	W	T	F	S	S
						01			01	02	03	04	05			01	02	03	04	05						01	02	01	02	03	04	05	06	07					01	02	03	04
02	03	04	05	06	07	08	06	07	08	09	10	11	12	06	07	08	09	10	11	12	03	04	05	06	07	08	09	08	09	10	11	12	13	14	05	06	07	08	09	10	11
09	10	11	12	13	14	15	13	14	15	16	17	18	19	13	14	15	16	17	18	19	10	11	12	13	14	15	16	15	16	17	18	19	20	21	12	13	14	15	16	17	18
16	17	18	19	20	21	22	20	21	22	23	24	25	26	20	21	22	23	24	25	26	17	18	19	20	21	22	23	22	23	24	25	26	27	28	19	20	21	22	23	24	25
23	24	25	26	27	28	29	27	28						27	28	29	30	31			24	25	26	27	28	29	30	29	30	31					26	27	28	29	30		
30	31																																								

ALL SOULS' DAY

THURSDAY 02

THINGS TO DO/NOTES

FRIDAY 03

THINGS TO DO/NOTES

SATURDAY 04

THINGS TO DO/NOTES

GUY FAWKES NIGHT

SUNDAY 05

THINGS TO DO/NOTES

JULY	AUGUST	SEPTEMBER	OCTOBER	NOVEMBER	DECEMBER
M T W T F S S	M T W T F S S	M T W T F S S	M T W T F S S	M T W T F S S	M T W T F S S
01 02	01 02 03 04 05 06	01 02 03	01	01 02 03 04 05	01 02 03
03 04 05 06 07 08 09	07 08 09 10 11 12 13	04 05 06 07 08 09 10	02 03 04 05 06 07 08	06 07 08 09 10 11 12	04 05 06 07 08 09 10
10 11 12 13 14 15 16	14 15 16 17 18 19 20	11 12 13 14 15 16 17	09 10 11 12 13 14 15	13 14 15 16 17 18 19	11 12 13 14 15 16 17
17 18 19 20 21 22 23	21 22 23 24 25 26 27	18 19 20 21 22 23 24	16 17 18 19 20 21 22	20 21 22 23 24 25 26	18 19 20 21 22 23 24
24 25 26 27 28 29 30	28 29 30 31	25 26 27 28 29 30	23 24 25 26 27 28 29	27 28 29 30	25 26 27 28 29 30 31
31			30 31		

NOVEMBER
WEEK 45

06 MONDAY
THINGS TO DO/NOTES

07 TUESDAY
THINGS TO DO/NOTES

08 WEDNESDAY
THINGS TO DO/NOTES

JANUARY	FEBRUARY	MARCH	APRIL	MAY	JUNE
M T W T F S S	M T W T F S S	M T W T F S S	M T W T F S S	M T W T F S S	M T W T F S S
01	01 02 03 04 05	01 02 03 04 05	01 02	01 02 03 04 05 06 07	01 02 03 04
02 03 04 05 06 07 08	06 07 08 09 10 11 12	06 07 08 09 10 11 12	03 04 05 06 07 08 09	08 09 10 11 12 13 14	05 06 07 08 09 10 11
09 10 11 12 13 14 15	13 14 15 16 17 18 19	13 14 15 16 17 18 19	10 11 12 13 14 15 16	15 16 17 18 19 20 21	12 13 14 15 16 17 18
16 17 18 19 20 21 22	20 21 22 23 24 25 26	20 21 22 23 24 25 26	17 18 19 20 21 22 23	22 23 24 25 26 27 28	19 20 21 22 23 24 25
23 24 25 26 27 28 29	27 28	27 28 29 30 31	24 25 26 27 28 29 30	29 30 31	26 27 28 29 30
30 31					

NOVEMBER

THURSDAY 09
THINGS TO DO/NOTES

VETERANS DAY [OBSERVED](USA)

FRIDAY 10
THINGS TO DO/NOTES

REMEMBRANCE DAY (CAN, AUS); VETERANS DAY (USA)

SATURDAY 11
THINGS TO DO/NOTES

REMEMBRANCE SUNDAY; DIWALI/DEEPAVALI

SUNDAY 12
THINGS TO DO/NOTES

JULY								AUGUST								SEPTEMBER								OCTOBER								NOVEMBER								DECEMBER						
M	T	W	T	F	S	S		M	T	W	T	F	S	S		M	T	W	T	F	S	S		M	T	W	T	F	S	S		M	T	W	T	F	S	S		M	T	W	T	F	S	S
					01	02			01	02	03	04	05	06						01	02	03							01				01	02	03	04	05						01	02	03
03	04	05	06	07	08	09		07	08	09	10	11	12	13		04	05	06	07	08	09	10		02	03	04	05	06	07	08		06	07	08	09	10	11	12		04	05	06	07	08	09	10
10	11	12	13	14	15	16		14	15	16	17	18	19	20		11	12	13	14	15	16	17		09	10	11	12	13	14	15		13	14	15	16	17	18	19		11	12	13	14	15	16	17
17	18	19	20	21	22	23		21	22	23	24	25	26	27		18	19	20	21	22	23	24		16	17	18	19	20	21	22		20	21	22	23	24	25	26		18	19	20	21	22	23	24
24	25	26	27	28	29	30		28	29	30	31					25	26	27	28	29	30			23	24	25	26	27	28	29		27	28	29	30					25	26	27	28	29	30	31
31																							30	31																					

NOVEMBER
WEEK 46

13 MONDAY
THINGS TO DO/NOTES

14 TUESDAY
THINGS TO DO/NOTES

15 WEDNESDAY
THINGS TO DO/NOTES

JANUARY							FEBRUARY							MARCH							APRIL							MAY							JUNE						
M	T	W	T	F	S	S	M	T	W	T	F	S	S	M	T	W	T	F	S	S	M	T	W	T	F	S	S	M	T	W	T	F	S	S	M	T	W	T	F	S	S
						01			01	02	03	04	05			01	02	03	04	05						01	02	01	02	03	04	05	06	07				01	02	03	04
02	03	04	05	06	07	08	06	07	08	09	10	11	12	06	07	08	09	10	11	12	03	04	05	06	07	08	09	08	09	10	11	12	13	14	05	06	07	08	09	10	11
09	10	11	12	13	14	15	13	14	15	16	17	18	19	13	14	15	16	17	18	19	10	11	12	13	14	15	16	15	16	17	18	19	20	21	12	13	14	15	16	17	18
16	17	18	19	20	21	22	20	21	22	23	24	25	26	20	21	22	23	24	25	26	17	18	19	20	21	22	23	22	23	24	25	26	27	28	19	20	21	22	23	24	25
23	24	25	26	27	28	29	27	28						27	28	29	30	31			24	25	26	27	28	29	30	29	30	31					26	27	28	29	30		
30	31																																								

THURSDAY   16
THINGS TO DO/NOTES

FRIDAY   17
THINGS TO DO/NOTES

SATURDAY   18
THINGS TO DO/NOTES

SUNDAY   19
THINGS TO DO/NOTES

JULY	AUGUST	SEPTEMBER	OCTOBER	NOVEMBER	DECEMBER
M T W T F S S	M T W T F S S	M T W T F S S	M T W T F S S	M T W T F S S	M T W T F S S
01 02	01 02 03 04 05 06	01 02 03	01	01 02 03 04 05	01 02 03
03 04 05 06 07 08 09	07 08 09 10 11 12 13	04 05 06 07 08 09 10	02 03 04 05 06 07 08	06 07 08 09 10 11 12	04 05 06 07 08 09 10
10 11 12 13 14 15 16	14 15 16 17 18 19 20	11 12 13 14 15 16 17	09 10 11 12 13 14 15	13 14 15 16 17 18 19	11 12 13 14 15 16 17
17 18 19 20 21 22 23	21 22 23 24 25 26 27	18 19 20 21 22 23 24	16 17 18 19 20 21 22	20 21 22 23 24 25 26	18 19 20 21 22 23 24
24 25 26 27 28 29 30	28 29 30 31	25 26 27 28 29 30	23 24 25 26 27 28 29	27 28 29 30	25 26 27 28 29 30 31
31			30 31		

NOVEMBER
WEEK 47

20 MONDAY
THINGS TO DO/NOTES

21 TUESDAY
THINGS TO DO/NOTES

22 WEDNESDAY
THINGS TO DO/NOTES

JANUARY							FEBRUARY							MARCH							APRIL							MAY							JUNE						
M	T	W	T	F	S	S	M	T	W	T	F	S	S	M	T	W	T	F	S	S	M	T	W	T	F	S	S	M	T	W	T	F	S	S	M	T	W	T	F	S	S
						01			01	02	03	04	05			01	02	03	04	05						01	02	01	02	03	04	05	06	07				01	02	03	04
02	03	04	05	06	07	08	06	07	08	09	10	11	12	06	07	08	09	10	11	12	03	04	05	06	07	08	09	08	09	10	11	12	13	14	05	06	07	08	09	10	11
09	10	11	12	13	14	15	13	14	15	16	17	18	19	13	14	15	16	17	18	19	10	11	12	13	14	15	16	15	16	17	18	19	20	21	12	13	14	15	16	17	18
16	17	18	19	20	21	22	20	21	22	23	24	25	26	20	21	22	23	24	25	26	17	18	19	20	21	22	23	22	23	24	25	26	27	28	19	20	21	22	23	24	25
23	24	25	26	27	28	29	27	28						27	28	29	30	31			24	25	26	27	28	29	30	29	30	31					26	27	28	29	30		
30	31																																								

NOVEMBER

WEEK 47

THANKSGIVING DAY (USA)

THURSDAY   **23**

THINGS TO DO/NOTES

FRIDAY   **24**

THINGS TO DO/NOTES

SATURDAY   **25**

THINGS TO DO/NOTES

SUNDAY   **26**

THINGS TO DO/NOTES

JULY							AUGUST							SEPTEMBER							OCTOBER							NOVEMBER							DECEMBER						
M	T	W	T	F	S	S	M	T	W	T	F	S	S	M	T	W	T	F	S	S	M	T	W	T	F	S	S	M	T	W	T	F	S	S	M	T	W	T	F	S	S
					01	02			01	02	03	04	05	06					01	02	03						01		01	02	03	04	05					01	02	03
03	04	05	06	07	08	09	07	08	09	10	11	12	13	04	05	06	07	08	09	10	02	03	04	05	06	07	08	06	07	08	09	10	11	12	04	05	06	07	08	09	10
10	11	12	13	14	15	16	14	15	16	17	18	19	20	11	12	13	14	15	16	17	09	10	11	12	13	14	15	13	14	15	16	17	18	19	11	12	13	14	15	16	17
17	18	19	20	21	22	23	21	22	23	24	25	26	27	18	19	20	21	22	23	24	16	17	18	19	20	21	22	20	21	22	23	24	25	26	18	19	20	21	22	23	24
24	25	26	27	28	29	30	28	29	30	31				25	26	27	28	29	30		23	24	25	26	27	28	29	27	28	29	30				25	26	27	28	29	30	31
31																					30	31																			

NOVEMBER
WEEK 48

27 MONDAY
THINGS TO DO/NOTES

28 TUESDAY
THINGS TO DO/NOTES

29 WEDNESDAY
THINGS TO DO/NOTES

JANUARY	FEBRUARY	MARCH	APRIL	MAY	JUNE
M T W T F S S	M T W T F S S	M T W T F S S	M T W T F S S	M T W T F S S	M T W T F S S
01	01 02 03 04 05	01 02 03 04 05	01 02	01 02 03 04 05 06 07	01 02 03 04
02 03 04 05 06 07 08	06 07 08 09 10 11 12	06 07 08 09 10 11 12	03 04 05 06 07 08 09	08 09 10 11 12 13 14	05 06 07 08 09 10 11
09 10 11 12 13 14 15	13 14 15 16 17 18 19	13 14 15 16 17 18 19	10 11 12 13 14 15 16	15 16 17 18 19 20 21	12 13 14 15 16 17 18
16 17 18 19 20 21 22	20 21 22 23 24 25 26	20 21 22 23 24 25 26	17 18 19 20 21 22 23	22 23 24 25 26 27 28	19 20 21 22 23 24 25
23 24 25 26 27 28 29	27 28	27 28 29 30 31	24 25 26 27 28 29 30	29 30 31	26 27 28 29 30
30 31					

ST ANDREW'S DAY (SCOTLAND)

THURSDAY 30
THINGS TO DO/NOTES

FRIDAY 01
THINGS TO DO/NOTES

SATURDAY 02
THINGS TO DO/NOTES

FIRST SUNDAY OF ADVENT

SUNDAY 03
THINGS TO DO/NOTES

JULY	AUGUST	SEPTEMBER	OCTOBER	NOVEMBER	DECEMBER
M T W T F S S	M T W T F S S	M T W T F S S	M T W T F S S	M T W T F S S	M T W T F S S
01 02	01 02 03 04 05 06	01 02 03	01	01 02 03 04 05	01 02 03
03 04 05 06 07 08 09	07 08 09 10 11 12 13	04 05 06 07 08 09 10	02 03 04 05 06 07 08	06 07 08 09 10 11 12	04 05 06 07 08 09 10
10 11 12 13 14 15 16	14 15 16 17 18 19 20	11 12 13 14 15 16 17	09 10 11 12 13 14 15	13 14 15 16 17 18 19	11 12 13 14 15 16 17
17 18 19 20 21 22 23	21 22 23 24 25 26 27	18 19 20 21 22 23 24	16 17 18 19 20 21 22	20 21 22 23 24 25 26	18 19 20 21 22 23 24
24 25 26 27 28 29 30	28 29 30 31	25 26 27 28 29 30	23 24 25 26 27 28 29	27 28 29 30	25 26 27 28 29 30 31
31			30 31		

DECEMBER
WEEK 49

04 MONDAY
THINGS TO DO/NOTES

05 TUESDAY
THINGS TO DO/NOTES

06 WEDNESDAY
THINGS TO DO/NOTES

JANUARY
M	T	W	T	F	S	S
						01
02	03	04	05	06	07	08
09	10	11	12	13	14	15
16	17	18	19	20	21	22
23	24	25	26	27	28	29
30	31					

FEBRUARY
M	T	W	T	F	S	S
		01	02	03	04	05
06	07	08	09	10	11	12
13	14	15	16	17	18	19
20	21	22	23	24	25	26
27	28					

MARCH
M	T	W	T	F	S	S
		01	02	03	04	05
06	07	08	09	10	11	12
13	14	15	16	17	18	19
20	21	22	23	24	25	26
27	28	29	30	31		

APRIL
M	T	W	T	F	S	S
					01	02
03	04	05	06	07	08	09
10	11	12	13	14	15	16
17	18	19	20	21	22	23
24	25	26	27	28	29	30

MAY
M	T	W	T	F	S	S
01	02	03	04	05	06	07
08	09	10	11	12	13	14
15	16	17	18	19	20	21
22	23	24	25	26	27	28
29	30	31				

JUNE
M	T	W	T	F	S	S
			01	02	03	04
05	06	07	08	09	10	11
12	13	14	15	16	17	18
19	20	21	22	23	24	25
26	27	28	29	30		

THURSDAY 07
THINGS TO DO/NOTES

FEAST OF THE IMMACULATE CONCEPTION; FIRST DAY OF HANUKKAH

FRIDAY 08
THINGS TO DO/NOTES

SATURDAY 09
THINGS TO DO/NOTES

SUNDAY 10
THINGS TO DO/NOTES

JULY							AUGUST							SEPTEMBER							OCTOBER							NOVEMBER							DECEMBER						
M	T	W	T	F	S	S	M	T	W	T	F	S	S	M	T	W	T	F	S	S	M	T	W	T	F	S	S	M	T	W	T	F	S	S	M	T	W	T	F	S	S
					01	02		01	02	03	04	05	06					01	02	03							01			01	02	03	04	05					01	02	03
03	04	05	06	07	08	09	07	08	09	10	11	12	13	04	05	06	07	08	09	10	02	03	04	05	06	07	08	06	07	08	09	10	11	12	04	05	06	07	08	09	10
10	11	12	13	14	15	16	14	15	16	17	18	19	20	11	12	13	14	15	16	17	09	10	11	12	13	14	15	13	14	15	16	17	18	19	11	12	13	14	15	16	17
17	18	19	20	21	22	23	21	22	23	24	25	26	27	18	19	20	21	22	23	24	16	17	18	19	20	21	22	20	21	22	23	24	25	26	18	19	20	21	22	23	24
24	25	26	27	28	29	30	28	29	30	31				25	26	27	28	29	30		23	24	25	26	27	28	29	27	28	29	30				25	26	27	28	29	30	31
31																					30	31																			

DECEMBER
WEEK 50

11 MONDAY
THINGS TO DO/NOTES

12 TUESDAY
THINGS TO DO/NOTES

13 WEDNESDAY
THINGS TO DO/NOTES

JANUARY								FEBRUARY								MARCH								APRIL								MAY								JUNE						
M	T	W	T	F	S	S		M	T	W	T	F	S	S		M	T	W	T	F	S	S		M	T	W	T	F	S	S		M	T	W	T	F	S	S		M	T	W	T	F	S	S
						01					01	02	03	04	05				01	02	03	04	05							01	02		01	02	03	04	05	06	07						01	02	03	04
02	03	04	05	06	07	08		06	07	08	09	10	11	12		06	07	08	09	10	11	12		03	04	05	06	07	08	09		08	09	10	11	12	13	14		05	06	07	08	09	10	11
09	10	11	12	13	14	15		13	14	15	16	17	18	19		13	14	15	16	17	18	19		10	11	12	13	14	15	16		15	16	17	18	19	20	21		12	13	14	15	16	17	18
16	17	18	19	20	21	22		20	21	22	23	24	25	26		20	21	22	23	24	25	26		17	18	19	20	21	22	23		22	23	24	25	26	27	28		19	20	21	22	23	24	25
23	24	25	26	27	28	29		27	28							27	28	29	30	31				24	25	26	27	28	29	30		29	30	31						26	27	28	29	30		
30	31																																												

DECEMBER
WEEK 50

THURSDAY 14
THINGS TO DO/NOTES

LAST DAY OF HANUKKAH

FRIDAY 15
THINGS TO DO/NOTES

SATURDAY 16
THINGS TO DO/NOTES

SUNDAY 17
THINGS TO DO/NOTES

JULY							AUGUST							SEPTEMBER							OCTOBER							NOVEMBER							DECEMBER						
M	T	W	T	F	S	S	M	T	W	T	F	S	S	M	T	W	T	F	S	S	M	T	W	T	F	S	S	M	T	W	T	F	S	S	M	T	W	T	F	S	S
					01	02		01	02	03	04	05	06					01	02	03						01				01	02	03	04	05					01	02	03
03	04	05	06	07	08	09	07	08	09	10	11	12	13	04	05	06	07	08	09	10	02	03	04	05	06	07	08	06	07	08	09	10	11	12	04	05	06	07	08	09	10
10	11	12	13	14	15	16	14	15	16	17	18	19	20	11	12	13	14	15	16	17	09	10	11	12	13	14	15	13	14	15	16	17	18	19	11	12	13	14	15	16	17
17	18	19	20	21	22	23	21	22	23	24	25	26	27	18	19	20	21	22	23	24	16	17	18	19	20	21	22	20	21	22	23	24	25	26	18	19	20	21	22	23	24
24	25	26	27	28	29	30	28	29	30	31				25	26	27	28	29	30		23	24	25	26	27	28	29	27	28	29	30				25	26	27	28	29	30	31
31																					30	31																			

DECEMBER
WEEK 51

18 MONDAY
THINGS TO DO/NOTES

19 TUESDAY
THINGS TO DO/NOTES

20 WEDNESDAY
THINGS TO DO/NOTES

JANUARY	FEBRUARY	MARCH	APRIL	MAY	JUNE
M T W T F S S	M T W T F S S	M T W T F S S	M T W T F S S	M T W T F S S	M T W T F S S
01	01 02 03 04 05	01 02 03 04 05	01 02	01 02 03 04 05 06 07	01 02 03 04
02 03 04 05 06 07 08	06 07 08 09 10 11 12	06 07 08 09 10 11 12	03 04 05 06 07 08 09	08 09 10 11 12 13 14	05 06 07 08 09 10 11
09 10 11 12 13 14 15	13 14 15 16 17 18 19	13 14 15 16 17 18 19	10 11 12 13 14 15 16	15 16 17 18 19 20 21	12 13 14 15 16 17 18
16 17 18 19 20 21 22	20 21 22 23 24 25 26	20 21 22 23 24 25 26	17 18 19 20 21 22 23	22 23 24 25 26 27 28	19 20 21 22 23 24 25
23 24 25 26 27 28 29	27 28	27 28 29 30 31	24 25 26 27 28 29 30	29 30 31	26 27 28 29 30
30 31					

DECEMBER
WEEK 51

THURSDAY 21
THINGS TO DO/NOTES

WINTER SOLSTICE

FRIDAY 22
THINGS TO DO/NOTES

SATURDAY 23
THINGS TO DO/NOTES

CHRISTMAS EVE

SUNDAY 24
THINGS TO DO/NOTES

JULY								AUGUST								SEPTEMBER								OCTOBER								NOVEMBER								DECEMBER						
M	T	W	T	F	S	S		M	T	W	T	F	S	S		M	T	W	T	F	S	S		M	T	W	T	F	S	S		M	T	W	T	F	S	S		M	T	W	T	F	S	S
					01	02			01	02	03	04	05	06					01	02	03							01			01	02	03	04	05							01	02	03
03	04	05	06	07	08	09		07	08	09	10	11	12	13		04	05	06	07	08	09	10		02	03	04	05	06	07	08		06	07	08	09	10	11	12		04	05	06	07	08	09	10
10	11	12	13	14	15	16		14	15	16	17	18	19	20		11	12	13	14	15	16	17		09	10	11	12	13	14	15		13	14	15	16	17	18	19		11	12	13	14	15	16	17
17	18	19	20	21	22	23		21	22	23	24	25	26	27		18	19	20	21	22	23	24		16	17	18	19	20	21	22		20	21	22	23	24	25	26		18	19	20	21	22	23	24
24	25	26	27	28	29	30		28	29	30	31					25	26	27	28	29	30			23	24	25	26	27	28	29		27	28	29	30					25	26	27	28	29	30	31
31																							30	31																				

DECEMBER
WEEK 52

25 MONDAY
THINGS TO DO/NOTES

CHRISTMAS DAY

26 TUESDAY
THINGS TO DO/NOTES

BOXING DAY; ST. STEPHEN'S DAY (ROI)

27 WEDNESDAY
THINGS TO DO/NOTES

JANUARY							
M	T	W	T	F	S	S	
						01	
02	03	04	05	06	07	08	
09	10	11	12	13	14	15	
16	17	18	19	20	21	22	
23	24	25	26	27	28	29	
30	31						

FEBRUARY						
M	T	W	T	F	S	S
		01	02	03	04	05
06	07	08	09	10	11	12
13	14	15	16	17	18	19
20	21	22	23	24	25	26
27	28					

MARCH						
M	T	W	T	F	S	S
		01	02	03	04	05
06	07	08	09	10	11	12
13	14	15	16	17	18	19
20	21	22	23	24	25	26
27	28	29	30	31		

APRIL						
M	T	W	T	F	S	S
					01	02
03	04	05	06	07	08	09
10	11	12	13	14	15	16
17	18	19	20	21	22	23
24	25	26	27	28	29	30

MAY						
M	T	W	T	F	S	S
01	02	03	04	05	06	07
08	09	10	11	12	13	14
15	16	17	18	19	20	21
22	23	24	25	26	27	28
29	30	31				

JUNE						
M	T	W	T	F	S	S
			01	02	03	04
05	06	07	08	09	10	11
12	13	14	15	16	17	18
19	20	21	22	23	24	25
26	27	28	29	30		

DECEMBER
WEEK 52

THURSDAY 28
THINGS TO DO/NOTES

FRIDAY 29
THINGS TO DO/NOTES

SATURDAY 30
THINGS TO DO/NOTES

SUNDAY 31
THINGS TO DO/NOTES

NEW YEAR'S EVE

JULY						
M	T	W	T	F	S	S
					01	02
03	04	05	06	07	08	09
10	11	12	13	14	15	16
17	18	19	20	21	22	23
24	25	26	27	28	29	30
31						

AUGUST						
M	T	W	T	F	S	S
	01	02	03	04	05	06
07	08	09	10	11	12	13
14	15	16	17	18	19	20
21	22	23	24	25	26	27
28	29	30	31			

SEPTEMBER						
M	T	W	T	F	S	S
				01	02	03
04	05	06	07	08	09	10
11	12	13	14	15	16	17
18	19	20	21	22	23	24
25	26	27	28	29	30	

OCTOBER						
M	T	W	T	F	S	S
						01
02	03	04	05	06	07	08
09	10	11	12	13	14	15
16	17	18	19	20	21	22
23	24	25	26	27	28	29
30	31					

NOVEMBER						
M	T	W	T	F	S	S
		01	02	03	04	05
06	07	08	09	10	11	12
13	14	15	16	17	18	19
20	21	22	23	24	25	26
27	28	29	30			

DECEMBER						
M	T	W	T	F	S	S
				01	02	03
04	05	06	07	08	09	10
11	12	13	14	15	16	17
18	19	20	21	22	23	24
25	26	27	28	29	30	31

NOTES

NOTES

NOTES

2024

JANUARY

M	T	W	T	F	S	S
01	02	03	04	05	06	07
08	09	10	11	12	13	14
15	16	17	18	19	20	21
22	23	24	25	26	27	28
29	30	31				

FEBRUARY

M	T	W	T	F	S	S
			01	02	03	04
05	06	07	08	09	10	11
12	13	14	15	16	17	18
19	20	21	22	23	24	25
26	27	28	29			

MARCH

M	T	W	T	F	S	S
				01	02	03
04	05	06	07	08	09	10
11	12	13	14	15	16	17
18	19	20	21	22	23	24
25	26	27	28	29	30	31

APRIL

M	T	W	T	F	S	S
01	02	03	04	05	06	07
08	09	10	11	12	13	14
15	16	17	18	19	20	21
22	23	24	25	26	27	28
29	30					

MAY

M	T	W	T	F	S	S
		01	02	03	04	05
06	07	08	09	10	11	12
13	14	15	16	17	18	19
20	21	22	23	24	25	26
27	28	29	30	31		

JUNE

M	T	W	T	F	S	S
					01	02
03	04	05	06	07	08	09
10	11	12	13	14	15	16
17	18	19	20	21	22	23
24	25	26	27	28	29	30

JULY

M	T	W	T	F	S	S
01	02	03	04	05	06	07
08	09	10	11	12	13	14
15	16	17	18	19	20	21
22	23	24	25	26	27	28
29	30	31				

AUGUST

M	T	W	T	F	S	S
		01	02	03	04
05	06	07	08	09	10	11
12	13	14	15	16	17	18
19	20	21	22	23	24	25
26	27	28	29	30	31	

SEPTEMBER

M	T	W	T	F	S	S
						01
02	03	04	05	06	07	08
09	10	11	12	13	14	15
16	17	18	19	20	21	22
23	24	25	26	27	28	29
30						

OCTOBER

M	T	W	T	F	S	S
	01	02	03	04	05	06
07	08	09	10	11	12	13
14	15	16	17	18	19	20
21	22	23	24	25	26	27
28	29	30	31			

NOVEMBER

M	T	W	T	F	S	S
				01	02	03
04	05	06	07	08	09	10
11	12	13	14	15	16	17
18	19	20	21	22	23	24
25	26	27	28	29	30	

DECEMBER

M	T	W	T	F	S	S
						01
02	03	04	05	06	07	08
09	10	11	12	13	14	15
16	17	18	19	20	21	22
23	24	25	26	27	28	29
30	31					